First Love

an anthology

The Make It Safe Project

Edited by Amelia Roskin-Frazee

Published in 2021 by The Make It Safe Project
San Francisco, CA
makeitsafeproject.org

First Edition
ISBN: 978-0-578-87753-2

Printed in the United States of America

Table of Contents

Foreword

by Amelia Roskin-Frazee

In 2010, I walked into my middle school's library, the warm yellow light a stark contrast to the cold feeling I felt creeping up and down my arms in layers of goosebumps. I found the computer the farthest from the door, the screen facing away from the prying eyes of the librarians at the front desk.

I opened up the library catalog search page. My fingers shook, catching on the corners of the keys, as I typed "LGBTQ" (lesbian, gay, bisexual, transgender, questioning or queer) into the search box. I moved the black and white mouse to the "Search" button and clicked it, the sound echoing through the room. The search page flinched, the computer dissecting the library catalog until finally it spit out a list: *No results.*

Of course, some books existed in 2010 for youth that contained LGBTQ characters or themes, but they were hard to find — tucked away underneath pages of Google results for Young Adult books, hidden behind labels warning parents that the books were for older readers.

In 2011, I began sending the books I could find — including some of my favorites like *Annie on My Mind* by Nancy Garden, *Ash* by Malinda Lo, and *Kicked Out* edited by Sassafras Lowry — to schools, youth homeless shelters, and juvenile detention centers; however, it never felt like enough. While I remain grateful to all the authors who have helped give a voice to a group that needed a voice more than ever, I kept wondering whether the books I sent fully represented the experiences of queer and trans youth. Many of the books I could find initially were written by white cisgender authors years removed from listening to the cracking sound of lockers closing in school hallways. Few people in the media and writing world dared write about the positive things — the first loves, first kisses, first moments of self-acceptance.

In 2018 when The Make It Safe Project started a writing scholarship for queer and trans youth, I didn't know what to expect; I certainly never imagined I'd get to read beautiful poems about secret first kisses during slumber parties, memoirs analyzing cultural taboos about sexuality, and same-sex romance short stories set on spaceships in the future. Yet this anthology, a compilation of the best submissions from the first three years of the writing scholarship, brings us all of those things.

The authors in this anthology — including winners Donovan Thomas, Eliana Lazzara, and Erin Samantha Hanson and runners up Jordan Elbualy, Danny, and TyAnna Melissa Farmer — bring us stories of love, fear, discrimination, rebellion, and liberation. They encourage us to learn about the reality they experience daily underneath headlines about the legalization of gay marriage. Even more daring, they challenge us to imagine what the world could be. Most of the submissions are written by queer and trans youth of color. The authors come from many backgrounds: some live with disabilities, some have experienced homelessness, some have experienced violence, some are religious or questioning or transitioning. I thank all of them — those who chose to share their names *and* those who asked to remain anonymous — for bearing their souls here to give other youth the library catalog search results I did not get in middle school, and to give you the chance to experience alongside them the power of first love.

3/24/17

by Donovan Thomas

2018 Scholarship Winner

My head is a place filled with thoughts,
Thoughts that never get the chance to be spoken into existence,
Easy as it seems for others to articulate their opinions,
I just let mine go unheard,
That is how my life has been,
Silence,
Listening to others speak,
Thoughts being put, no forced into my head,
Words inscribed onto my heart,
They aren't mine,
They are foreign,
Intruding upon my existence,
Suppressing my self-expression,
Your love is perverse,
Unholy,
God vomits at the sight it,
Put some bass in your voice,
Boys don't talk like that,
Boys don't dress that way,
Comb that nappy hair,
No, matter of fact cut that stuff
Within these moments I realize that my self deprecation
Stems from my lack of validation,
And excess of parental altercations
Creating toxic situations,
Black boy
Black boy breaks barriers,
Boy too black to be held back,

Boy too gay he can't be black,
That boy not black
He gay,
He gay,
He gay,
Black and gay don't mix,
Gay and black is like crack, wack,
black gay boy holds the world on his shoulders,
gay black boy's back cracks under pressure,
Covered by the sea of welts left by their clever quips and whips
black gay boy comes home,
Parents greet him with welcoming smiles,
Bible in hand,
Tells that black gay boy he can't be black and gay,
Holy water splashes in black boys faces,
Anointed oil drips down his face,
Taking place of his tears,
Now that boy black, gay, and broken
Broken,
Boy, That boy is broken,
The headline reads "Teen Dies From Open Rebuke,"
They say eyes are the gateway to the soul,
Well mine are constantly rolling
At all the things people try to force onto me,
I am not your robot,
I will think freely,
I will not serve your white Jesus,
I will combat your system
While fulfilling my mission,
I have the perfect vision,
I will resist,
I control my own destiny,

Create my own reality,
I am queer,
I am black,
But, I am not your negro,
I will resist,
You can't control me,
I won't be silenced,
You can no longer mold me,
I will resist,
I will wear my tight jeans,
Comb my hair when I please,
Challenge your standards with ease,
I will resist,
And realize,
Realize,
You may not recognize me,
But I'm here,
Yeah,
I'm here.

Missing Pieces

by Erika Jung

When I was in the 5th grade my friend and I were hanging out on the swing set
Her little sister came over and asked us what the word gay meant
We both laughed and told her to be quiet
It was as though she had said the "f-word"
Or had asked us where babies come from
We explained what it meant
But quietly so no adult could overhear
Then she asked if two women could love each other
We laughed again
Told her that she would learn about it when she was older
Because at this age she was too young to know

It's like completing a puzzle without the right pieces
So the picture on the box doesn't match the pieces you've been given
So you try to create a sunset out of a rainforest
But while everyone has red pieces you only see green
So you paint over your parts to create the picture others want you to make
Cutting and gluing the pieces together so they can fit within one another

It's like trying to play poker
But you've been dealt a hand of UNO cards
So while the others play their royal flushes
You are trying to play your wild cards
So you lose your chips
While the other players reap the rewards

It's like trying to communicate to someone who speaks French
When you only speak English
And have been handed a Spanish dictionary

So everything sounds like gibberish
And you cannot even say hello

It's like trying to run a race in stilettos
And you cannot walk in heels
So when everyone sprints in their running shoes
You are miles behind
Tripping over your own feet

How can you be expected to finish a puzzle with the wrong pieces
To win a game of poker with the wrong cards
To speak a language you've never understood
To run a race with the wrong start
To put words to your feelings
When nobody teaches them to you

The Invisible Rainbow

by Riley Newman-Gatton

Where am I
I wander the pages of the history book
I know I'm in here somewhere
The book is massive
There is still something missing

The red bricks thrown at Stonewall aren't here

I read the page on Abraham Lincoln
The secrets of his heart aren't here
I know he is one of us
But you can't trust the books
Not the ones the schools give you
They'll never tell you anything

The orange light of the Castro streetlamps aren't here

Where am I
I know I'm in here somewhere
I call out to Eleanor Roosevelt
She recites her love letters to Lorena
She writes of longing and hope
But they don't put those in the book

The yellow buses that wouldn't take kids with AIDS to school aren't there

Where am I
I can hear the sounds of the Civil Rights Movement
It lingers from the chapter behind me
I hear Martin Luther King, but not Bayard Rustin

Something else happened in D.C.
They don't put that in the book

Cleve's quilt covering an expanse of green isn't here

Where am I
Stories of New York City are everywhere in this book
Founding Fathers mingle with Ellis Island immigrants
Something else happened in New York
They don't put that in the book

Marsha P's body floating on a blue river is absent

Where am I
The book goes back further than I thought
But I still can't find any of us
I can remember reading stories of Ancient Greece
Renaissance Italy
There is still something missing

Sappho's code of violets isn't here

How can this be?
Where is the rainbow?
Where am I?
Where are we?

My Identity Through Poetry

by Alex

conventionality

what is conventional?
the establishment of a norm?
the perception of a norm?
the conformity to a perceived norm?

whatever the case may be
i am not conventional

i have tried to be conventional
in my mind
conventionality was normalness
conventionality was assumed
conventionality was aspired after

even if it wasn't real

straight hair, straight shoelaces, straight everything
was straightness conventional?
if straightness equivocates conventionality
and conventionality equivocates normalness
was i not normal?

no
i am not conventional

practice what you preach

you claim to celebrate our differences
i have screamed to others that
i am different
my experiences
my identity
my soul
my life
they are all so different from yours
but you cannot comprehend
and that lack of comprehension does not turn to celebration

i learn not to scream my differences
because it may cost me my life
Matthew Shepard, Howard Efland, Blaze Bernstein
countless others
i have seen them pay that price

the book you made me read

the book is titled
"one man's journey back to God"

the title says what you cannot
or perhaps what you do not want to say
back
to
God

and i am left to wonder
if i need to find my way back
when did i abandon god?

when i told you who i am?

or

when i realized who i am?

if my being means i am estranged from god

was i ever his child?

if my being means i am estranged from god

can i ever be found?

i can never stop being

so i am left to wonder

when did god abandon me?

undone

do you remember when you called me a sinner?

you tried to justify it

we are all sinners, you said

do you remember when you read that bible verse?

you tried to support it

god can forgive, you said

but

i am not a sinner, i said

i tried to defend myself

will i ever forget the shock and the hurt?

a sin can be forgiven, it can be undone, i said
i tried to explain
why can't you understand that i cannot be undone?

even today these questions go unanswered
i can answer these questions
can you?

luke

one day the world may discover us
in the dark
the feeling his wings have over me
let them
i am ready for the light
and yet perhaps
we are the light
and the rest of them
are in the dark

constellation

they say that each of us has our own star
a celestial being under which we were born
so i look to the night sky
and amidst
the ever stretching
the all consuming
black

i try to find mine
a small glimmer amidst an overpowering sky

the cynic in me believes that
life does not make sense
the scatter of stars strewn across the sky do not form images
yet we see constellations
and because perception is reality
the scatter of stars become stories, images, life

sometime
somehow
someway
our stars crossed paths
collided really
for the light that we create could only be brought into existence through collision
and we formed a constellation
our own story

others will soon appreciate its beauty

life is math

life is like math
your experiences, traits, personality
all add up to you
it is addition

yet for me
my life is subtraction

i subtract my ethnic identity to blend with my white peers
i subtract my american identity to connect with my culture
asian-american or american-asian
why not
asian+american
why must i choose a side
why must i subtract half of my identity
why do you only want to see me as
asian
or
american

white normativity

when i go to starbucks
i am "so white"
yet starbucks is a normal teenage activity
why do we equivocate normalness to whiteness?

intersectionality

gay asian
those two words intersect to make the word
gaysian
me
believe me
i am unbelievably proud
yet homophobia from the ethnic community stifles my identity
and racism from the queer community stifles my culture
both communities fight tirelessly for equality

yet they fight within their own lane
they ignore where the two lanes intersect
they ignore intersectionality
so i am left with no one to fight for me
however
i will fight for me

Overcoming Fear One Step at a Time

by Anonymous

There is not a day in my life where I do not think about the outcome that my sexuality will have on my family, especially my father.

I am a Mexican gay teenager from Illinois. I am the youngest out of five siblings and the only person in my family who identifies as gay. Growing up in a Catholic household I have always known that being gay is wrong and not accepted by many. My parents have also said that it is everyone's decision to be with who they want to be. They say this because no parent ever thinks about their child being gay, so I do not know how they will react when I tell them that I like men. Having a very religious mother and a father who grew up in a "machista" environment in Mexico has made life rather difficult because I feel as if I am living a life hiding in my own shadow. My entire life I have lived in fear of being disowned and not being accepted by my family for being gay.

As long as I can remember I have always known that I've been gay. Since a young age, I have always found myself attracted to men. The first person that I told about my sexuality was my best friend Vanessa in 2008. I remember this day as if it were yesterday. We were eight years old. We were playing outside during recess on our elementary school playground. Vanessa was the first person with whom I felt comfortable talking about my sexuality and she was the first person to accept me for who I was. In school I was always bullied for being the boy with the "girly" voice, the boy who would write like a girl, and the boy who would always hang out with the girls. I would constantly be told to act manlier and hang out with the boys, but I never felt right doing that. I always felt more comfortable with the girls because with them I could be open and not feel judged for who I was. With Vanessa, I never felt judged and I felt the love of a true friend. As time went by, I started to tell more of my girl friends and eventually there was a group of my closest friends who knew about my sexuality.

When I started middle school, people began coming up to me and asking me if I was gay. I was still not prepared to let the world know about my sexuality, so I always denied everything that they asked me. A big part of my fear had to do with my nephew being a year younger than me. I constantly would think about how things would go down if he found out about my sexuality at school. He would tell my family, and my biggest fear was for my family to find out by someone else instead of me. All throughout middle school I kept hearing those same comments I heard in elementary school and kept getting asked about my sexuality.

Then, my 8th grade year the unexpected happened: I was still not ready to come out to my family, but on September 13, 2013, my two older sisters found out that I was gay. I came home from school and was sitting at my kitchen table when I showed my oldest sister, Esther, a picture on Facebook. While I was on Facebook, I was messaging my other best friend Allie and I was telling her about my boy crush at school. The moment I showed my sister the picture on Facebook, I received a message from Allie. My sister Esther said that she was going to check my messages to see what I was doing, and my first response was "No," which led me to lock my iPod immediately.

In that moment I felt as if the world was coming down upon me. I began to cry in front of my sisters Esther and Victoria and all I heard was Esther say, "Give me the passcode." My sister wasn't going to let me leave until she went through my messages. All I did was cry and then I noticed her begin to get mad. She told me one last time, "Give me the passcode."

I knew that she was frustrated already, so I said, "It's 0-6-1-3." As she typed in the passcode I cried louder and louder and I finally shouted the words, "I'm sorry. I'm gay."

The moment I said these words I felt such a huge weight lifted off my shoulders. I pleaded and begged my sisters to not tell my parents anything because I was afraid of being disowned. Both of my sisters hugged me and said, "No matter what you will always be our little brother and we will always love you." Hearing these words from them gave me hope that maybe my family wasn't going to push me away. All I've ever wanted is for my family to accept me for who I am and accept me no matter my sexual preference.

After my sisters found out about my sexuality, I began to feel more comfortable with myself and a couple of months later I started high school. My first two years of high school I was still in the closet, but many people already had an idea about my sexuality. Then my junior year I began accepting that I was gay, and all my friends accepted me for who I was. Instead of my friends pushing me away, like I thought they were going to, they all showed me their support. Being open about my sexuality at school allowed me to open up myself with others, but I still live with the fear of coming out to my parents, especially my father.

This past summer I graduated high school and made the decision to come out to my mother. On August 15, 2018, I came out to my mom three days before I moved to college. Coming out to my mom has been one of the hardest things I have experienced in my life. I told my mom that I did not want to be rejected by her and that I wanted her to love me.

My mother was very supportive of me and told me, "No matter what, you will always be my son." She said that just because I was gay it didn't make me any different from the rest of her children.

I explained to her that I feared getting disowned and that I have always lived with the fear of not being loved by her and my father. I told her that I was not ready to come out to my father.

My mom respected my decision by saying, "Your father doesn't have to know. What you told me stays between you and I."

Coming out to my mom and three days later leaving for college in a different state has been the hardest decision that I have ever made in my life.

The next step in my journey of coming out is to tell my father. I have had a constant battle with myself on when I should tell him, and although I am terrified, I think that I have mentally prepared myself to tell him when I go home from college. I am 18 and I just want to live my life freely without being afraid. I want to be able to experience dating and hopefully one day introduce a partner to my parents. I know that by building my courage, I will be able to overcome this fear and hope for the acceptance and love of my father.

Years in the Life

by Jordan Elbualy

2018 Scholarship Runner Up

his name is sami daoud and he is seven years old, and he has moved to a new city.
seven years old is his baba leaving for long hours, working long jobs, but coming back smiling.
it is his mama trying her hardest to make ends meet without their family to support them
and scraping by.
seven years old is the new school, the new language.
it is the neighborhood boys calling to him to come play, his running to catch up.
seven years old is not knowing their language, their words, but knowing how to play their games.
it is peaceful, with hours spent talking to his twin sisters, malika and maysa.
and most of all, seven years old is happiness.

his name is sam daoud and he is eight years old, and he is learning how to fit in.
eight years old is the new name, the american name, the new school's name.
it is his baba working only one job, finally, and his mama thinking about college for malika and maysa, happily.
eight years old is trying to learn the cropped words the boys say, trying to learn the names of their favorite bands, movies, sports stars, because none of that ever seems to come naturally to him.
it is spending hours in front of the tv, imitating the people's voices and learning, always learning.
eight years old is not really knowing what his work means yet, but knowing that it will help him be like the other kids.
it is trying to feel like the neighborhood boys, to make everything perfect

and normal, but never succeeding.
and most of all, eight years old is looking up.

his name is sam, just sam, and he is nine years old, and he has the world figured out.
nine years old is asking his mama and baba to call him sam, asking them to speak english when the boys come to play.
it is his sisters telling him off for his mispronunciation of arabic words, making him gargle so he doesn't lose his ayns and ghayns.
nine years old is befriending the older boys in an attempt to seem more like a boy, befriending their families to seem more like an american.
it is eating hamburgers and hot dogs with the neighbors instead of coming home.
nine years old is figuring out school, figuring out social circles.
it is laughing at the jokes the boys make in an effort to seem more like them, even though he knows malika and maysa would kill him if they knew.
and most of all, nine years old is looking for acceptance.

his name is sammy (with two ms and a y) and he is ten years old and he is slowly realizing what life is like for people like him.
ten years old is teaching his sisters what they call american, teaching them how to stop the words from skipping through their still-heavy accents, part arab, part new yorker, barely the smooth speech of their neighbors.
it is watching his mama instruct his sisters how to go on a plane, instructing them how to be the quiet, docile, friendly american that she says the men in the airport can't see in them.
ten years old is seeing malika and maysa hug his parents, seeing them walk through a plastic arch.
it is seeing a tall man pull them both aside, pointing to their hijabs, and malika glancing back at him, afraid.
ten years old is hearing his mama sobbing at night, hearing his baba's consoling and yet empty words, devoid of any real ability to confirm or

deny anything.
it is wondering what will happen when he goes to college, what the tall man will say to him.
and most of all, ten years old is about realization.

his name is sami daoud again and he is eleven and he isn't sure what's going on anymore.
eleven years old is tumbling into middle school, tumbling into new classes with new teachers who couldn't care less about how to pronounce his name.
it is meeting a new group of kids who laugh at his name and make fun of his still noticeable accent.
eleven years old is not knowing why his skin is different than the skin of the new kids, not knowing why they care.
it is waiting for malika or maysa to call so he can talk in the arabic he once hated.
eleven years old is living in the school library, living in the stacks of books that can't shout at him like the kids at school do.
it is finding solace in the stories of adventurers and swashbucklers, residing in worlds of magic and mystery so infinitely better than his own.
and most of all, eleven years old is about coping.

his name is still sami daoud and he is twelve years old and he is trying to make a place for himself.
twelve years old is trying to keep up with the neighborhood boys, trying to keep up with their constant flow of slang in a language that has suddenly become again unintelligible to him.
it is hearing the new phrases slip from their mouths, hand-me-downs from their parents.
twelve years old is rethinking playing with the neighborhood boys, rethinking his relationships and himself.
it is malika and maysa returning from their first year of college wide-eyed and talkative, telling stories of their classes and the people they've met.

twelve years old is seeing maysa going out without her hijab, seeing his baba speak quietly and quickly to his mama behind maysa's back.
it is malika telling him all about her classes on psychology and gender and how interesting the world really is.
and most of all, twelve years old is learning of a new perspective.

his name is sami daoud and he is thirteen years old and he is trying to process what he sees through the eyes malika and maysa have given him.
thirteen years old is teetering on the beginning of a new start, teetering on the edge of an ending.
it is learning more and more about everything he possibly can, under malika's guidance, of course.
thirteen years old is talking to the librarians constantly, talking enough that sometimes they bring books from home on science and philosophy and identity for him to read.
it is ignoring his classmates, who whisper about how he never talks.
thirteen years old is reassessing his life in segments, reassessing his existence small bits at a time.
it is maysa bringing him to the city to meet some of her friends from college, different and wild people with hair dyed strange colors and beautiful, outlandish clothing, all of them talking quickly and laughing loudly.
thirteen years old is trying his hardest to find a group to call home, trying his hardest to find people to relate to in the small town so unlike the big city.
it is begging maysa to again bring him with her, longing for another taste of the world beyond his own.
and most of all, thirteen years old is discovering his own perspective.

their name is possibly sami daoud and they are fourteen years old and they are finding their niche in the world, ish.
fourteen years old is starting over, starting high school in a place with more students and a bigger library than ever.

it is befriending the other kids who don't align with their town's normality, like maysa's friends, like sami themself.
fourteen years old is discovering a world they didn't even know existed, discovering a world where the expectations their parents implied of binary and beauty became more like suggestions.
it is spending less time engulfed in stacks of books and more time running around their town with their new friends in the dim, warm light of the streetlamps.
fourteen years old is finding a yemeni friend, finding someone their age to talk to in the language they've come to love.
it is their baba smiling when he hears them speaking arabic to him again.
and most of all, fourteen years old is a beginning.

their name is samiya daoud and they are fifteen years old and they are in a time of transition, in every sense of the word.
fifteen years old is malika and maysa finishing college, an era in their lives over while at home another era in their life is unfolding.
it is malika deciding to go back to school, getting her master's degree in psychology, to their baba's pride and delight, and maysa deciding to move into the city, starting her life as a stylist to the city's rich and famous, to their baba's pride and dismay.
fifteen years old is introducing maysa to their friends, introducing maysa to the brightly colored family she'd always been a part of.
it is college looming on the horizon, their mama printing out lists of top colleges and their baba pestering them about their classes and standardized tests and scholarships.
fifteen years old is changing their name, changing the way they think about themself.
it is finding their way back to the librarians, telling them all the stories they've lived over the years.
and most of all, fifteen years old is choices.

their name is samiya daoud and they are sixteen years old and they are experiencing a mild upheaval.
sixteen years old is their baba announcing that he has been promoted, announcing a move to another town, miles and worlds away.
it is saying their goodbyes to their friends, a final ma'a salama to the colorful group of friends they've come to know as family.
sixteen years old is driving into the now familiar city to see maysa, driving to see someone they love for the last time, at least in this era of his life.
it is smiling when maysa offhandedly calls them by their new name, the happiness that comes with knowing the people they love love them for themself.
sixteen years old is turning a corner onto a new street, turning a corner onto a new life.
it is a bittersweet ending of an era, a true fresh start.
and most of all, sixteen years old is new.

their name is samiya daoud and they are seventeen years old and they are adapting surprisingly well to their new state of change.
seventeen years old is gearing up for the end of yet another phase of their life, gearing up for the start of another.
it is trying to decide on a college, on a major, on a career, a life, talking over the phone to malika endlessly about applications.
seventeen years old is disappearing into their school's library again, disappearing into a world of studying and test scores.
it is completely devoting themself to getting into the world beyond their small town, new and yet, somehow, the same.
seventeen years old is contemplating telling their mama and baba about their new name, contemplating telling them about their new happiness.
it is crying with relief when their acceptance letter to the school in the city arrives.
and most of all, seventeen years old is hope.

her name is samiya daoud and she is eighteen years old and she is finally herself.
eighteen years old is settling into her new identity, settling into her new city.
it is standing tall as the airport security officer looks her up and down and refusing to be humiliated.
eighteen years old is running through the night with her new friends, running with a pack of people who wear glitter on their faces and hold hope in their hearts.
it is reveling in her new life as samiya daoud, whom maysa has dubbed girl wonder, and malika has, amused, embraced.
eighteen years old is wearing her new hijab home, wearing it amidst the endless explanations she gives to her baba, who, eventually, smiles and nods, giving his approval.
and most of all, eighteen years old is happiness.

10:19

by Serenity Powell

I've identified as lesbian since 6th grade and I've never once worried that my sexuality could result in me getting hurt
That was at least before pride fall was a thing
Now I have to look over my shoulder to make sure no one is following me
Being told to take the stuff I'm most proud of out of my Instagram bio
All because I have to fear that I'll be harassed because I'm lesbian
I wish there was someone with a brave voice to stand before us
Stand before me but I guess I have to be that brave voice
And I fear I may not be brave enough
May I be protected for the war has only just begun

Dreams of Pride

by Anonymous

it is difficult to celebrate pride when your parents view it with shame
difficult, but not impossible
carefully you hide the queer books and movies from your parents' view
concealed like addicts hide bags of white
you hide yourself
you wear pride shirts at night, safe from their judgmental eyes
a rainbow in the dark

and when religious talk turns to condemnation and hellfire
unwitting judgement of their own daughter
you swiftly retreat to your private bathroom
stare in the mirror and declare "you are not a sin"
but whisper softly
some things they aren't ready to hear

but let yourself dream of a day in the distance
a family of tradition breakers like you
banners of color swirl around you
and you fill your lungs and scream of *love love love*

yet for the moment be content with this —
to be proud of yourself
your quiet pride

Ongoing Victories

by Kendall Hovius

Content warning: discussion of hate crimes

But what are you passionate about?
What makes words fall from your lips like stars,
And sends adrenaline running through your veins?
But what makes you cry?
What grips your heart and tugs, and now you're leaking like a broken faucet?
But what do you live for?
What sits in your bones and weaves into your DNA and fills up all the empty places left inside your chest where family and friends who now hate you used to live?
But what would you die for?
Who would you die for?
What things would you give your heart for,
Still beat-beat-beating in your chest like the shots in the Pulse night club, or the ones you don't hear about in California, or Texas, or just Google it at this point there's too many to remember.
Most of us are already dead before the last breath leaves our body.
We are ghosts, on our knees, begging for a taste of human decency,
"Oh please, let me live, let me exist in your world for just a second"
When you don't fit in, you get death threats.
Jesus hates me, and they'll cleanse my sinning flesh with asphalt in any alley anywhere.
There's a certain limit when you become desensitized to something like this.
Ask any queer person, and they'll tell you.
But sometimes it's easier, because you know how they view you,
Maybe it's as a freak, a plague, but it's not a question, masquerading in friendliness.
I have spent years fighting to even remove one single letter from what people call me,

I've fought with blood, and tears, and small victories that I've dragged kicking and screaming.
It took me 16 years to get to this point,
You can't stop me, you can't keep me quiet. I'm never going to fit your normal and I don't care.
And still you have the nerve to ask me
"But … what's in your pants?"

Now Unformed but Not Forever

by Rachel Thompson

God, I sit in my room and I yell inside because
I don't know who I am?
Am I a girl? Or a boy? Or something in between?
I had this figured out
Once, then twice,
But I keep going back
To confusion,
And not to You like I should.
And it's all so complicated,
I struggle to like myself
(even though I know I'm Your masterpiece),
This weird physical form. My legs
Are strong, my hands gentle,
My voice clear,
But
It doesn't all fit, I think.
I want to metamorphose
Transform, reach my final evolution.
I only wish that I knew what form it would take
Maybe then I could speed it up?
I know that journeys take time,
Rome wasn't built in a day, and neither will I be.
I'd still like to know.
Please Lord?
I understand that
You are a busy person, I don't want to
Make demands of You.
I think—
If you just remind me you love me,
Like you love the starlings and eagles,

I'll be okay.

Because with your love,

I know I don't need wings to fly

Caged

by Myles McMahon

Suffocating
This cage
That I must call mine
Born into what is not in mind
This body
Horrifying to my eye
Why is the boy not me?
Why must I suffocate under her?
"Miss"
"Darling"
"Sweetie"
Those words so sickening when describing me
I want his freedom
But no
Born with two x's
I suffocate
Because my body decided to be she
While my mind
Says he

On Secrets, On Dreams, On Ribbons

by Sarah Cheyney

I am not a lesbian. I am not a lesbian. I am *not* a lesbian.

The grey ceiling looks down at me. Whatever you say, ceiling says. I'm not the one who can't go into the girls' locker room without thinking about Nancy Huntington and her white thighs, and her red uniform, and her white thighs …

Shut up! I throw my pillow at the ceiling. It smacks soundlessly and falls back onto the carpet. The ceiling is silent. It looks down on me and says nothing when I burrow my head into the pillow and squeeze my eyes shut to erase all visions of red uniforms and swaying, swaying, hips.

Sleep, however, is not silent. It is chattering, noisy, filled with a susurrus of Nancy peeling her sweater off in the dressing room, the scratch of Nancy's pencil on lined paper in class, Nancy laughing and cradling her denim purse. I am running through the corridor because I cannot escape Nancy — up the stairs, to the roof. The night is black and full of stars that flicker and twinkle and kiss. *You cannot escape*, they tell me, *so stop running.* Instead, I jump — straight off the roof, plunging below. I flop into a swimming pool. I am too tired to continue, so I float. Nancy appears beside the diving board, swishing her blonde hair and smiling at me. *I'll rescue you. Come here*, she says, and then the pool is a dark bliss and we are two yellow kissing stars.

***

Nancy really is in the dressing room the next morning. I don't look at her. I can't, not when I am so full of shame and tenderness. These dreams follow me around in the day. If they stayed under the cover of night, waiting for my return to sleep, I wouldn't be so scared. But they wake up and grab at the spare space in my mind, packing themselves in tightly and threatening to spill all these strange urges and desires in the open light.

Nancy offers me her good-luck ribbon for the next few tournaments. She tells me it helped her pass a lifeguarding test.

Clumsily, she stands by my side and threads the fabric into my braid. Her fingers brush my scalp, which tingles and shakes and dances at the touch. I stand very still. I am afraid to breathe. She hovers at the side of my vision, a golden blur. If I look too closely and her smudged edges materialize into sharp lines, a concrete face, I might lean in and kiss her. Her hands are weaving. My hands are wringing. She glazes over as I blink.

I say, "It's beautiful. Thanks, Nancy."

I am so tender — for her lips, for her golden tresses, for the way she holds her left wrist loosely in her right hand, for the four-and-a-half seconds she holds my eye contact — that I swear I will fall apart and separate, meat from the bone, all my individual bits and pieces curdled by longing.

Please, God, never let anyone find out that I'm a … that I'm … about my feelings for Nancy.

***

The court is hot and sunny and the sky is clear. I'm sweating, taking big gulps of dry air which brush and tickle my throat. I keep watch on the stands in case Nancy comes, even though I try and pull my attention away — eye on the ball, eye on the ball, watch the ref … but as soon as I let my guard down, in little moments after I swig from the water bottle or when I swipe the sweat from my forehead, I crane my neck to the stands and search through unfamiliar faces. *Come on, Susan,* I plead to myself. *I'm just curious. Let me hope.*

In the last match she comes, waving and beaming. I am acutely aware of her eyes on my shoulders, swinging back and forth, muscles tensing and gripping, relaxing. I feel as though I am putting on a secret show. I wonder if she sees it too.

She is waiting for me in the locker room. "You star!"

I smile weakly. "It was the ribbon." Now that we are alone, both here, I'm not entirely sure what to do.

She starts to unthread the ribbon from my hair. I turn to face her, but she doesn't move, so I maneuver awkwardly under her arm. We giggle in a mess of limbs and ribbon. Nancy is so close, and she is like a dream, and I am trembling. Nancy is so close, and her hair is wet, and I can see the sunburnt skin peeling off on the top of her nose.

Nancy is so close now that I lean forward, I brush our noses together, and I kiss her. There is no distance between us at all as she kisses me back. I reach up, hesitantly, to touch the back of her head. Her hair is fine and soft, like cotton candy. Her lips are sweet, and so I close my eyes and I am at the fair, fireworks exploding above, heady air all around, cotton candy in my hand, cotton candy in my mouth.

Then we part. She is staring at me. I lean in, and she pushes me away.

"I can't … this is wrong, Susan. Why did you do that? God, Susan! Why do you make me feel like this? I can't, I can't …" She is breathing heavily.

"I thought you liked it."

"That's not the point." She moves away from me. I scramble after her but she says, "Get away from me. I will not let you make me a sinner." She swings open the door. I catch it. She pushes me away. "Don't tell anyone. Ever. Got it? Promise me, Susan."

I am nodding. Then Nancy is far, receding into the distance.

I can't quite look anyone in the eyes on my way out. I could not bear the weight if my friends, peers, family knew about my dreams … their eyes, their thoughts. I think about Nancy pointing accusingly. I think about Amy, tugging at her little sister's arm and pulling her away from me. I think about my mother, crying, my life, wavering and shimmering and distorting like hot air that rises from the sidewalk grates. I just want to turn back time, or maybe erase my own existence, like a little white mark on the chalkboard snubbed into nothingness.

I have another game tomorrow. Nancy is not in the locker room in the morning. She does not come to any of my matches. If she is at the sports center at all, she is hiding from me. I wear her good-luck ribbon. As the days pass, my disgrace, my fear, and my shame mount. Nancy becomes some kind of a blur in my memory, a blip in my summer, a feverish dream come to life.

I resort to keeping her ribbon in the first drawer of my bureau. Sometimes I touch it gently. Sometimes I weave it through my hair like a secret talisman. I cannot control my dreams about her; they come and go, bringing seas of stars and cotton candy and bright kisses that illuminate the black night behind my eyelids. Still, I keep my promise. No one knows.

Wasting Away in the Closet

by Lizzie Lohrer

There's an ache that fills you
When you have to hide a part of yourself,
When you're forced to shove it into the closet,
Pile old clothes on top of it,
Lock the door and hope that no one finds the key.

There's an ache when you have to bite your tongue
At Christmas dinner,
When you have to tell your grandmother that no,
You aren't seeing anyone right now,
Because it's easier to lie
Than to try and get her to understand the truth.

There's an ache when you hear that
Your grandfather is in the hospital,
And though you know with all your heart
That he wouldn't understand this part of you,
That he would be ashamed and upset,
It still hurts to think about him dying
Without knowing the truth.

You don't realize how large this part of you is,
How important your queerness is to your identity
Until you can't talk about it,
Until you're talking with your brother
And have to hold back a joke
Because you haven't come out to him yet,
Not even because he wouldn't understand,
But because there hasn't been a good time to tell him.
Not yet, maybe not ever.

There's something that TV doesn't mention
About being queer,
Which is that coming out isn't a one-time thing.
You have to do it again and again.
You have to constantly make that decision about whether or not
To mention it in casual conversation.
Straight people can talk about their love life anytime,
But when it's you, that raises questions.
Coming out isn't just putting a pride flag in your Instagram bio —
It's deciding to argue with your classmate
Who just said something homophobic.
It's deciding to use feminine pronouns
When talking about the girl you have a crush on.
It's sitting down with your friends at lunch and crying
While telling them, and having to ask your best friend
Over and over again
If she's okay with it because you keep expecting her to change her mind.
It's having to tell all of your friends one by one,
And being stressed every time
Because you aren't sure if they're going to accept you.
It's constantly exposing this personal part of yourself,
Again and again and again and again and again,
And hoping to be met with understanding instead of judgment.

And sometimes, being queer means choosing not to fight that battle,
Because you don't have the strength to argue with someone
For the fifth time that week.
Sometimes it's sitting in quiet discomfort
While your classmates discuss queer issues
Like one might discuss their takeout order.
Sometimes it's not correcting your aunt when she talks about
Your future husband and kids.

Sometimes it's taking the pride pin off your bag when you go to church,
And saying "boyfriend" instead of "girlfriend"
When you talk to your older neighbors.

It's constant evaluation and decision making
And lies of omission that become second nature.
It's crying in the shower because
You just got your heart broken but can't tell your parents.
It's writing poetry and then deleting it,
Or ripping it up,
Or stuffing it in the bottom of a drawer
So that no one can find it.
It's hiding parts of yourself in a closet,
Zipped up in the suitcase you never use,
With the door locked and the key
Sitting under your tongue,
Reminding you of what's at stake every time you go to talk.

It's exhausting. It takes so much of you all the time
Just to hide that part of yourself away,
But you know that you need to.
The world isn't ready to hear you speak.
You keep sitting there, with your hand raised,
Wanting just a minute of their time,
A tiny bit of respect.
But they keep not calling on you,
So you sit, and keep your hand up,
Silent and waiting for the right time
While a part of you wastes away in the closet.

Relentless

by Blessen H.

Meet me on the island away from yesterday.
Meet me in Paris away from the feeling you may try to forget.
Meet me far away and love me; touch me.

Stay.
Be here in the moment and feel me.
Stay long enough to feel me, and to see me.
Could you ever see me in my truest form?
Am I worth transgressing from norm?

Seek me among the crowd
That is so loud
And destructive of my efforts.
I am still here,
Relentless to your acknowledgement.

Believe me, it is extremely difficult to see life plainly,
So hard to believe the loathe that others release.
But believe me, my love can expand from sea to sea.

It is a sight to see if you would
Meet me on an island as it hones a new day.
Meet me anywhere, away to new perspectives,
For feelings you may never forget.
Meet me far away and love me, and touch me
Because I am human too.

Love will speak when we meet,
And maybe you will see how love can be broken
When we do not love relentlessly.

My love is love.
It meets to stay,
And seeks to believe.

Coloring Books

by Kimi L.

We never left our coloring book days

We're told to color in the lines.
The straight, harsh lines.
The lines of "acceptance"
That "make you normal."
When we spill over the lines
They come to cut off the extra "waste"
To cut off the outliers
To cut off the different

We're told to color in the lines
With the colors they want
But not the colors we have
And the colors we are.
When we let ourselves show
They hide us under their "perfect pictures"
And shame our feelings
And shame our hearts

We're told to color in the lines
But we don't always fit
We're not gingerbread people
With cookie-cutter lives.
When will they realize that
We can't change how our heart beats
Or who we love
Or who we are

We're told to color in the lines

But not every happy ending
Needs a prince and a princess
In a fairy tale castle.
When will they accept that
“Hetero-Ever-After” isn’t the only objective
Since boys can love boys
Since girls can love girls

And we can’t stay in our coloring book days

Coming Out

by Faith Vargas

Content warning: physical violence

Just blurt it out! Why aren't you talking? I thought to myself. I had invited my best friend over to do exactly that: talk. But I fell silent and as hard as I tried, I couldn't find any words to say. So we sat in silence as she awkwardly smiled.

"So what were you going to tell me?" Ana asked. I wanted to shout it right there, *I'm gay!* But my mouth failed to move and I was frozen. "Faith, what's going on?"

The image of my mother immediately flew through my mind. She had said the exact same thing to me six months ago. I was sitting in my room, listening to music and reading when she entered. She held my diary in hand, opened on the page that described my inner turmoil over a crush. As Ana said the phrase with kindness and worry, my mother said it with anger and disgust. She slammed the diary on the ground and slapped me.

I clutched my face, unable to discern the vivid memory from reality. I saw the look of concern on Ana.

"Ana, I really have to tell you something," I said as my voice quivered.

"Faith, I'm here for you," Ana said with a hushed voice, as if I was a hurt child. Ana always had a way of making you feel comforted with her baby-like voice. It wasn't working now though, to my dismay. "What do you have to say?"

My mother appeared back across my mind, saying the exact same phrase. She held me by the collar, crying. She showed me the page of my diary, hoping I had a worthy explanation. Perhaps a simple, *I was just kidding.* But I wasn't kidding. This is who I am and I have to deal with it every day. My mother fell to her knees, clutching on the diary as if she was holding onto my youth and innocence. She was holding onto the possibility that I would get married to a man and have children and have a "normal" life. I have to snap out of this déjà vu.

"Ana, I'm … I'm g—" I couldn't even finish my phrase. I choked on my words as a tear fell down my face. I could see Ana's eyes lock with mine. I said it in my mind and I said it with my eyes. *I'm gay.* I could almost hear Ana saying back, *It's okay*, with those kind eyes. She placed her hand on my shoulder, showing me trust and compassion I had never experienced before.

I was thrust back into my memory with the feeling of a hand on my shoulder. I remembered the feeling of my mother grasping my shoulder, tightly holding onto me as I sobbed. And then hitting me once again, as if to create balance. She turned towards the wall and punched it, instead of me. My face stung and blood dripped on the floor. The red below me matched my mother's face as she grew more angry.

I uttered the same phrase I did six months ago with the same hushed tone: "I'm gay." I said it with the exact same fear and sadness and disgust, awaiting Ana's eventual anger.

She moved closer to me and I flinched, in preparation. But, to my surprise, she hugged me.

She whispered something I had never heard, "I love you. I accept you."

Gemini Rising

by Sarah Metz

I've never understood astrology.
I'm a gemini rising,
Whatever that means.
I'm reminded of this whenever I look at her.
"You're a gemini rising, you just want to be her friend"

I guess I don't understand astrology.
They never say this when I look at him.
It's never "you're a gemini rising"
It's always "just ask him out"
It's always "this is correct"

I don't understand astrology.
Whenever I talk about her I'm met with the same response.
No matter how soft her eyes, how kind her voice,
How uplifting her spirit, how delightful her presence.
"You're a gemini rising, you just think wildly"

I really don't understand astrology.
They get even more concerned when I talk about them both.
His smile is comforting, her hands are like home,
Her generosity is inspiring, his humor is witty.
"You're a gemini rising, you're just indecisive, make up your mind"

I will never understand astrology.
Maybe it's for the best.
I don't think I want to understand.
I don't want to understand how something as simple as the time of my birth
Can validate some feelings and invalidate others.
I don't want to understand how the stars can bring people together,

But at the same time tell them it's wrong.
I'm a gemini rising,
Whatever that means.

I don't want to understand astrology.
I already understand myself.

The Thoughts of a Transgender

by Ash Spoonmore

Content warning: suicide

"A person is a person no matter how small."

I take these words and live by them. I write this to speak on what it's like. To be something, something so foreign to the normal human's mind.

Being transgender is like this: Everyday of your life, you have always wanted a dog. For as long as you can remember — even if you don't know to what extent — you have wanted one. You asked your parents, Santa, the Easter Bunny, even the Tooth Fairy. Then one day you get a dead cat for your birthday. You say, "This isn't a dog," but, "You get what you get and don't get upset." So you carry around and care for the dead carcass. All sorts of people look at you, unable to understand what you are doing.

So, then one day you decide to try to make it look a bit nicer. You wash it a bit, comb what little fur it has left, cover the decrepit limbs. But then you realize the ineffectuality in doing this all the time, because you are still carrying around a dead animal. So, you continue to carry it around because you must, no matter how horrible it maybe. Although you are carrying around a dead and rotting cat, you aren't a goddamn cat owner; you still want a dog.

I think sometimes about what it means to be transgender. I probe and probe for answers, because as the possibility for a new age of enlightenment and safety increases, the others want to know. I've come up with many answers, but I can hold to none. I don't deserve to paint the definition of a culture with the limited experiences I've had. I don't see myself in the transgender identified people allowed on television. I don't see myself in the transgender identified people making news feeds and giving high profile interviews. And as my nation's exposure to our culture increases, likely will their curiosity. Am I transgender? Do I have the right?

I've heard doctors, psychiatrists, may refuse transgender patients access to hormone therapy based on how dedicated or convincing their portrayal of their identified gender. If you want to be a man or woman, you'll have to look like the women and men on TV. If you want to be transgender, you'll have to look like the trans identified people on TV. Every single one of us who has an active role as either participant or observer in our society is prey to the crisis of legitimacy. Am I enough? Am I strong enough? Am I brave enough? Mom enough? Dad enough? Competitive enough? Successful enough? Rich enough? Sexy enough? Devoted enough? It never ends.

We're, as a nation of people, being crushed and catalogued by this ever-present lens, looming over us, exploiting our weaknesses and fears so it may grow wider, and support itself as it follows us, seemingly forever into the future. And one of the worst fears this camera of existential torment exploits, in most of us every day, is, "Do I have a reflection?" "What does it look like?" "Do I look like me?"

What does it mean to be transgender? I can't get away from that question. But I don't have an answer. There are varying degrees of anguish, depression, panic, anxiety, and other wonderful emotional states that creep up on you and breathe down your neck nearly every waking day. Absolute contempt for the lie of a life you've lived till now, and contempt for the fragments still stuck to you, in memories, attached to your body and mind. Fear of those in your own community who would purposefully humiliate, invalidate, or attack you, choosing their own universal moral code over the native urge and capacity to support the health and continued well-being of another human. A neighbor. A pupil. An employee. A sister, brother, son, daughter, mother, father, cousin, your own blood.

What is being transgender like?

By my experiences, it's just like being anyone else in the country. But with a lot more fear, death, exclusion and medication. "Just be yourself," they say, as if being transgender was the same as liking to wear funky sweaters or dying your hair every month. There's no fun in panicking over where to use the restroom, or the sting of pain when someone uses the wrong name or pronouns. Everyone has a picture that all transmen love women and sports, and transwomen love boys and dresses. They have yet to understand any difference and when they see it, it's constant question and judgement. If you want me to "just be myself," give me the right to do that without question. Don't look at my eyeliner and ask, "Are you still a boy?" Clothing does not invalidate gender. My gender is my choice, not yours.

To the Transgender Suicides,

The peace of acceptance once you are finished, put to earth, Life was harsher than the dirt, Parents made you feel worthless, because you wanted to wear a short dress, because you felt different, cut off, disowned, rejected. One friend after another disappears, and no one hears the sobs. No one feels the salty tears, No one holds your hands or offers you a hug. You were damned by the those who demanded you to conform, where there was no warmth. The clock cuts you bitterly condemning you to be lonely.

And you cry even more, knowing you won't be the only one. Not the only daughter wanting to be a son, Not the only male that wants to be female, Not the only soft face hardened, or hard face softened till the sorrow overflows. Till everyone you know closes the door and you disappear forever more. They say there is a brighter end of the tunnel, but the same tunnel is starting to look dark and gray.

I promise you, you must walk through the tunnel paved with chipped and rocky walls. There's more to you then you could ever see. There's so much more to this world you haven't laid your eyes on. Even the image in the mirror confuses you, you grab and push your body through all the pain. Still leaving you with this image. An image you don't recognize.

My fellow transgender, even if your family disowns you, even if people who you are close to, leave. Do not leave that image imprinted mirror the way you see it. Make a change. Make it the way you dream. How you see yourself. It may take years, months, days. But I promise thing that are amazing come in time. You must give yourself the chance. Do *not* get rid of your chance to finally be who you are.

I used to think I was all alone in feeling the way I do; I went through life wondering if there were others too. Now, I know I'm not alone and I can be myself and my fellow transgenders are always here for me in case I need some help. I wouldn't be here without you, my lovely transgender, I'd still be lost and hiding in my closet until the end turn dark and grey.

Sincerely,

Someone who survived

People who are transgender shouldn't have to fear going outside into the society of this world. They should be accepted no matter what circumstances against our beliefs. They are people too, not segregated second-class citizens. They should be able to walk outside their home without even thinking of the fact that they could be murdered.

In 2015, there were at least 21 transgender women who were the victims of murders across the United States. 2015 also marked the highest number of murders against transgender people on record. These murders were committed by both strangers and loved ones of the victims, and they have been classified as hate crimes by activists and by the people who were close to the victims. But until law enforcement consistently reports on the set of criteria that would classify transgender murders as hate crimes, the statistics that the FBI is required to release each year will fall short of being accurate.

While we do not yet have reliable statistics about murders and hate crimes against transgender people, as awareness increases that will likely improve.

While there are many ways to support transgender people — including activism — the most effective way to shrink the number of murders in the future is to compile and release accurate statistics that would show these crimes for what they are. Until then, these sad and gruesome crimes will continue to occur, and transgender people will continue to be victimized. These are people.

We are people and we deserve the right to be who we are and love who we want without harm.

White Washed

by TyAnna Melissa Farmer

2020 Scholarship Runner Up

A rainbow; red, orange, yellow, green, blue, purple … black.

Vibrant. Bright. Beautiful. Wise beyond years. But you are dark.

Dark as in the melanin in my skin. Bright as in the rainbow I have been forced to hide.

Beautiful afroed hair, dark, wise soul.

Surrounded in a sea of white, all that is seen is my black.

Seas of white, slowly rising.

Keep your head up. Hands forward. Keep swimming, they say.

White waves crash against you, you're suffocating.

They say breathe.

I can't, you say.

White waves crash against you. The white waves wash you of your brightness, dull you of your beauty, and drain you of your pigment.

The white waves have bleached your rainbow, flattened your Afro, and white washed you of your pride.

The Knife

by Diana Marino

gay
a word that is most disrespected
used as an insult or just thrown around for fun
by insensitive teenagers in your class
not thinking that a queer might be sitting
right in front of them

you feel attacked
as if arrows are being shot at you
yet they don't know who you love
but all at once
you want to stand up and say something
to tell them stop!
or ask why?
why do you use that word the way you do?
there is nothing wrong with it

but you know what they will do if you talk
"why so offended?" they will question
"are you …?"
and those of your same sex will want to move away
thinking you find anyone with the same genitals as you attractive
as if you were a disease

and if not, you will be judged
ridiculed for defending a community
you won't admit you must be a part of
if you care so much about it

you are revolting

an atrocity to be around

you would think everyone has already gotten with the time

so you keep your mouth shut
and let the insult of your existence be used
while the mouths of insolent children run as they will
then you go home
watch a show or movie you like
breathe easy from the everyday at school
and a scene will show on the screen
of two girls kissing in an embrace

and you will hear noises of disgust behind you
from your father
appalled by what he sees on the TV
you change the channel as he tells you to

no, he doesn't know either
and it's probably better that way
you don't wish for him to think of you
the way the kids at school do

you tell yourself that a lot
that it's for the best
yet you ache to tell someone
anyone that won't jab the knife at you
with the blade they say isn't there
because of the way that you are

or at least
the way you think you are

you're still a bit confused
maybe afraid
what if I'm lying?
but you know when that girl in math class
sat in front of you
you didn't have butterflies in your stomach for no reason

still, you reject it
and say you don't long for a 'love of your life'
because you know the truth

kids your age play stupid games
and don't treat each other the way they should
and it will always be that way
plus, you don't want to know what it's like
to have your heart broken

my family matters have already done that

so I won't
never will I look for a soulmate like everyone else
and play the dating game
of having dinner with strangers
that will eventually tear me to pieces

love is pain
and I think I've had enough
because in the end
it's another kind of knife
but one your partner holds

Dad, I'm Gay

by Achilles Wice

Dad, I'm gay.

Why wasn't I brave enough to tell him? I've kept this secret for so long, I almost right out told him last week so why, now that I've planned out what I'm to say, why can't I say anything at all? He should love me no matter what so what am I so scared of?

Dad, I'm gay.

He'll tell you he had a feeling this was coming. You've already cut your hair. He'll tell you it's just a phase. Tell that to the girl you've been in love with for the past two years. He'll tell you that you're confused because you have a gay friend, it's not you. You haven't spoken to that "friend" for who knows how long. He'll walk out of the room, yelling about how the "Democrats did it." You're not sure what an entire political party has to do with your coming out, but you nod in silence.

Listen to me! Your internal frustrations are so loud and clear that the ringing in your ear is the only proof that you've said those things. So you'll sit there in silence, wondering when his internal debate will subside so everything can go back to the way it was. He'll stop himself and ask why you were so nervous about telling him. Your lips quiver.

This. This is why you were so scared.

He'll tell you he's happy if you're happy but for some reason, you can't believe him.

He doesn't know that I'm more than gay. The only reason I said gay was because he wouldn't understand any other word I describe myself as. *Oh, hey dad! Yeah, I just wanted to let you know I'm a pansexual, non-binary trans masculine person and I'd appreciate it if you used he/they pronouns.* If those words ever made it out of my mouth, they'd be thrown back in with, "You'll always be my little girl," so I guess that's why.

Dad, I'm gay and you won't accept it, but this is the only way you'll know a part of who I am.

Dad, I'm gay because you'd have a heart attack if I told you everything at once.

Dad, I'm gay, but I'm still the same person that will play video games, go hunting and fishing with you, make mac n' cheese like it's a religion, and hug you every night because I'm your kid.

Dad, I'm gay, but please don't leave me.

The King and I

by F. Reilly

The first time I opened his door, it was an accident. I had locked myself in my room, bound my chest with a scarf, and stuffed a sock down the front of my jeans. I pulled my uncut curls under a cap and fanned the ends out over my forehead, mimicking a short fringe. I had a nervous little hunch that I was determined to test. I posed in my mirror, turning and admiring the shapes I had created for myself, and that was when I saw him. Reflected back at me, watching me with kind eyes set into what looked like my own face, was everything.

He wasn't actually me though, that much was clear. For one, there was no bulge under his shirt, either from his chest or from the thick scarf used to tie it back. His hair was short, and his sideburns ran lower than mine did. But more than that, he had something I didn't, something had clicked for him that hadn't yet clicked for me. He stared into my eyes, and I was pondering that when I heard footsteps outside my door. I startled, and he disappeared.

Shucking the scarf, the sock, the cap, I reminded myself, *If they catch you just say you were finishing your homework*, but it didn't matter. The knock on my door never came, and I changed into sweatpants and climbed into bed without seeing him again.

As I closed my eyes, I christened him the King and vowed to find him again.

***

That summer, I worked up the courage to cut my hair.

I pulled my best button up shirt — my only button up shirt — over a sports bra, which I wore inside out. I didn't see a difference, but I had heard that there was one. It was a two block walk to the nearest hair salon, and I shook with nerves the whole way there.

When I told the hairdresser what I wanted, she smiled, "You won't cry, will you?" I nearly broke out laughing.

As I felt the hair that had been mine falling around me, I started to relax, leaning back into the fabric of the chair and taking comfort in the metallic click of scissors around my head.

On the walk home, I couldn't stop running my hands through the coarse, cropped strands, and I rushed to the bathroom mirror as soon as I could. He was waiting for me when I stopped, giddy, to admire the cut. We looked more alike now, although I could finally pinpoint what the difference between us was. He was older. His jaw had filled out, and I could see hints of stubble along his cheeks, and just over his upper lip. He winked at me and smiled as if to say, *Keep it up, you're getting there.*

I learned what "butch" meant soon after, and I fell in love. I caught the eye of the King in my phone as I read the definition I had found, and both of us smiled at each other. I had heard about the click that others described, that moment when they discovered what they meant to themselves, but I hadn't believed it until then. My masculinity had finally found a direction to race towards, and I shot after it, doing as much as I could to keep up.

That was when drag first made its way into my life.

The drag king was wearing a beautiful, blinged out, sort of regency-style suit coat. I think he was going for Prince, and it absolutely worked. He leapt across the stage, flirting with the queens up with him as he went, making his way to the microphone. I had no idea how he got his voice that low, but he made it clear that he would be the emcee for the night, cracking charming jokes as he introduced the performers. I spotted the King out of the corner of my eye, reflected on to the dancefloor by the lights, seemingly standing on his own, a shimmering depiction of how I usually saw him. He was watching the stage, as transfixed as I was. In this light, I could've been his twin.

The first chance I got, I brought out the makeup I had and pulled up a YouTube tutorial on how to contour your face to pass as a man. It was meant for trans men, but the goal was the same. I didn't have much, so I dusted some grey eyeshadow under my chin and eyebrows, figuring I was just experimenting anyway. In the corner of my eye, I caught the King, watching me, motionless, from a corner of my mirror. I borrowed an eyeliner pencil from my mom's makeup and sketched a thin pencil mustache above my upper lip. I finished the look by using black eyeshadow to try to mimic stubble. I grabbed the sock again, just for added effect, and stepped back.

There was no denying it. I looked like a mess.

Regardless, I was elated. Past the mess, past the caked eyeshadow and strange contours and lopsided mustache, was me. I donned one of the newer button-ups I had acquired, stealing a tie from my dad's hook, and I strutted around the empty hallways of my house, singing poorly to whatever my playlist brought me and reveling in the moment. The King strutted with me, reflecting in picture frames and refracting in glass panes. He was proud, I think, of himself as well as me.

And so, we grew together. He'd appear in windows to toss a thumbs up my way when I successfully fielded a question about myself. He'd appear in movie theater bathroom tiles, to wink and make rude gestures at women who liked to glare at me. He'd appear in my own mirror, as I felt the pangs of dysphoria for the first time, smiling sadly and reminding me of what I could be. He always stayed one step ahead of me, a natural inch to my heeled and booted one, a genuine shadow to my cosmetic, a real beard to my illusion.

I had put on my face more over the years as well, learning to apply the contour in a way that made sense, learning to paint a mustache to make it look real. Or, more often than not, to just cut one from the tips of my hair. I got artsy about it too, drawing lipstick hearts over my eyes, making fake kiss stains along my arms, spiking my hair so I looked more punk, even mixing women's coats and shirts into my ensembles to get that pop that I so wanted. I started a social media profile for myself, to track my progress, and to perform the only way that I could. The King and I had a routine. On weekends, I'd get in drag and he'd watch, pointing out small errors in the mirror, then I'd take photos and stay dressed up while I edited, and by the end of it we'd have enough pictures to supply the account with until the next weekend. He'd appear in the photos, we tested it, but we never ended up posting any of him. He never showed any interest, and I, perhaps selfishly, was happy to keep my closest confidant to myself.

By the time I graduated, the account had grown significantly and I had managed to get myself into a handful of drag shows, although I never enjoyed them as much as I did the photography. I got a job, moved in with some friends, and was managing a side gig doing promo shoots for some of the queens I had met at the shows. The King had stuck with me throughout, I even kept a disco ball in my room to try to get him to appear as he did in front of that stage years ago. He never used it, so maybe the conditions were wrong. I only saw him like that, shining and haloed with joy, and all in the third dimension, one more time.

***

It was the last show I had planned on doing. I was still going to stay connected; it had gotten around in the local drag community that I was a good photographer to work with, but the stage had never been my strong suit.

I was just emceeing that night, and by the time I finished the first introduction, I regretted the jacket I was wearing. On a whim, I found time to go backstage and grab my body paints, then stripped to a white t-shirt and stood in front of a mirror, painting random, cartoonish tattoos across my arms. I won't lie, it was mostly an excuse to see the King. When he didn't appear before my cue back to the stage, I sighed, packed up my things, and went back out to continue the introductions.

The rest of the night went smoothly. I was having fun with everyone who came on stage — I knew most of them, and they were happy to mess with me on my last night.

During my last few minutes, he appeared. I was bidding everyone a goodnight, cracking a last few bad jokes, encouraging one more round of applause, and finally beginning to make my way offstage, when I saw him. He was standing on the dance floor, composed entirely of light, and smiling the biggest, proudest smile I had ever seen on him. I gave him a small salute, then stepped off the stage, into the darkness behind the curtains.

***

I see the King less these days. Sometimes I wonder if I made him up, if he was some kind of coping device until I figured myself out enough to not need him anymore. I like to think that he wasn't, though. I like to think that he was something else, someone who saw me and decided I needed a hint and a mentor. I like to think that I don't see him in mirrors, or windows, or raindrops, or beams of light because I can't tell the difference between us anymore. I even like to think that he wasn't that uncommon after all, that every little kid with new hormones and a confusion about mirrors has someone like him, to wink and smile and support them. But mostly, I'm not that naive.

I watch out for him still. My friends must think I'm self-obsessed for how often I examine reflections in shop windows. A sign would be nice, that I'm doing something right.

I work with kids at an LGBTQ center. I think at least some of them consider me to be a mentor, and that's really all I want. I try to be what he was for me, a reflection, not just of possibilities, but of definites. What they can be, what they will be, a guarantee that they can make it through. I've connected with all of them, but the ones that stick with me the most are the ones who are there by complete chance. Like I had so many years ago, they stumbled in by accident, or on a whim, and something clicked. They open my door, just as confused as I have been so many times, and I smile, and I wink, and I let them shine.

Willow

by Nicole Gonzales

Willow
a simple
yet beautiful name for a girl
for such a sight
with the most gorgeous curves
and the cutest smile.
short red hair
and subtle rosy cheeks so kissable

Willow
the girl to call
whether it's to talk you out of harm
or a simple cry

Willow
the girl that cannot save everyone
has lost those she's loved

Willow
the girl

Willow
Willo
Will

Will
the boy

Snip

by C.E.S.

Content warning: self-harm mention

Snip.

The first lock of hair hits the ground.
The split ends of my Plain Jane haircut shattering
Against my cold bathroom tiles.
A soft blond puddle
Dripping off my head,
Oozing, to the ground.

Snip.

The only sound is my shaky breath
Piercing the silence,
With a constant soft wheezing.
Each cut comes with a squeak,
As the rusty blades
Slide past each other.

Snip.

This time a tear falls too
A cold bead slipping down my cheek.
(As it had so many times before),
Slipping past the blush I cake on every morning,
As an attempt to please mother.
This tear bubbles over with pure, elastic, joy.

Snip.

Another lock. Another tear.
My hair swings under my ears now.
A sizable lake pooling around my ankles.
Drowning my pale toes,
A roaring river carrying away everything bad,
Everything is drifting away.

Snip.

My hair snuggles against my scalp,
Cozying into a comfortable spot.
The metal freezes my scalp with every chop,
Hair bits cling to the blades.
How many times have I dug these scissors
Into my wrists?

Click.

The scissors drop onto the pearly vanity.
My hands grip the edge.
The reflection staring back is finally me.
A boy.
Stumbling, but still going.
The ocean at his feet smooths the path.

The World with Five Letters

by Anonymous

Content warning: sexual harassment, bullying

Her life revolved around the number 5.

She was 5 when her reality's monochrome began unraveling. A way to describe it would be like blind people seeing for the first time, an overwhelmingness drowned with awe and curiosity. At 5 years old she was embraced by a monster whose horror she could not yet identify. She witnessed the evil of humanity at its finest but knowledge at 5 years old can be limited, so she paid no more attention to it.

Five years later she was in the fifth grade where she gradually learned more about herself and the world around her. At 10 years old she understood her encounter with the monster somewhat better and cried. She also learned from the kids around her that she was weird, a try-too-hard, and a poser. People were hurting her without even knowing it, but so was she. Her fifth-grade teacher had a flamboyant character, and she felt this need to always talk bad about him, saying things like "wow he's so gay" this and "wow he's so gay" that. Her upbringing taught her to be ignorant, she said. It raised her to believe that pure love only existed in one form and anything other than that was disgusting, a sin. In the fifth grade a girl said her hair was pretty and she could never look at her straight in the eyes after that. She wondered why she felt so weird around the girl, but knowledge at 10 years old could also be limited so she told herself that she just needed a friend.

In her culture, 15 is the year of womanhood. At this age she knew who she was but now she just wanted her knowledge to halt; ignorance really was bliss. Another girl came into her life, but this time she knew it was more than a platonic desire. She was infatuated, falling into a hole of anxious thoughts and self-destruction. She blamed her way of being on the monster. And at 15, she encountered another monster but this one was different. She was strong enough to escape before it could cause severe harm, but she felt too weak to ever speak up about it at the time. This monster disguised itself as an angel, and because of that, a part of her feared that no one would ever believe her. The other part is even more heartbreaking. She knew she was a victim, but she still feared that she did something wrong. She thought maybe it was her fault that the monster followed her, that maybe things would be different if only she had been more decorous.

They say you cannot love anyone else until you love yourself. On the fifth day of the fifth month, she had her first relationship with the same girl she became infatuated with at 15. Unfortunately, her heart was broken 5 days before September.

But also, something in her changed: she was no longer afraid, and she worked very hard to get there. She went through therapy, she practiced meditation, and she finally learned to accept herself. She found another girl. In fact, they found each other. She is now with someone who could listen to her speak for the rest of her life and would write about her on the laptop she got for Christmas.

We found each other, and I promise that we are never letting go. Aydee is my five-letter world.

Fingerprints

by Sebastian Dean

a fingertip
glides down my chest
dips into me
leaves
invisible
fingerprints on my thighs

a signature on a closing document
it tastes like
tears
and kisses
and nylon straps tied around my waist

a silicone wish rests in a box by your side
your hand on my cheek
your breath on my lips
your stamp burned on my neck
the closest thing to home I have felt in my life

our contract is folded neatly in a memory
decorated softly among many others
not to be unfurled until
the conditions are changed
or the terms are simplified
or home takes on a new meaning

The Box

by Tia

Content warning: disordered eating

I have a box with roses on the top. It's brown, and the roses are painted red, but the box is old, and so the red paint on the roses is chipping away until I can see the bare wood underneath. Sometimes, I find myself running a thumb across the roses, rubbing a little more paint off. I have to catch myself; I want the roses to stay red as long as I can. The box to stay perfect.

When I open my little brown box, up comes a dancer on a spring. I'd like to say she's porcelain, but I don't know if she really is. I'd know if she broke, but by then it wouldn't matter. When I open the box and she stands tall, one hand arching gracefully over her head, the music starts, and she spins to it.

She has a pretty blue skirt that encircles her tiny doll waist. When she twirls to the piano music, which is sorrowful or mysterious or full of potential depending on the mood I'm in, the skirt sometimes bounces up and down. It's very light, that skirt. Light, and a lighter blue than her ballerina leotard and tights.

Her shoes are the best part. Beautiful; she stands on the tips of her toes and I watch the shoes turn around and around. I watch the ribbons that climb up her legs like ivy reaching for the sun.

I open the box at least once a day. Usually more. I used to bring it with me everywhere, until my mother told me it was time to grow up. That the box was like my security blanket, and I needed to move away from it. She said I would get bored of the box, someday.

My mother is a liar.

I went to the ballet on a school trip when I was twelve. I remember the dancers, and their tulle skirts and powerful leaps. More than the dance, I remember the feeling afterwards — breathless. For the performers, and for me.

When I got home, I asked my mother to sign me up for lessons. She said no.

I didn't let up about the lessons. I asked her day after day. I locked myself in my room and opened my music box and watched the doll spin.

After a few weeks, I told my mother that if I still had a father, he would have let me dance, but I didn't have a father because of her. She cried, and I cried, but she signed me up for ballet lessons starting the next week, so I wasn't sorry.

I loved my lessons, even though I was awful at first. I got better and better, though. I thought about my box, and the dancer with her perfect hair and gently moving skirt and beautiful shoes, and I thought that I would be her. I thought this with a fervor and a passion that never left me, not as I grew and moved into pointe and came home with toes sore and bleeding, because it was what the dance asked of me and what I was ever so willing to give.

Once I had graduated high school, I went to school for dance. My mother and I fought. She swore she wouldn't pay for me to pursue something so useless, so risky. My mother didn't understand. She said I would regret everything and I left the house with my suitcases and my box tucked under my arm.

My mother is a liar.

I was near the top of my class at my new school. I was second best.

First best was Maria.

I thought I hated her at first. Because she was so perfect, and the praise I had once received was now lavished upon her. As I worked hard to become better, I told myself it was out of spite. Remember that graceful curve of your hand, more graceful than Maria's. Get that choreography right first time, faster than Maria.

And then it was the day after a hard practice. Maria and I had stayed late, just the two of us, and practiced in our corners of the room. I was by the mirrors. I didn't notice she had come over to me until she was there, standing so close, with her practice pointe shoes silent on the floor.

Maria was taller than I was, which meant she had to lean down to kiss me.

It smelled like dance studio, like work and sweat and blood and perfection, but it also felt like Maria. Pink and tulle, softness and roses.

I didn't hate Maria.

We danced together in the practice room, day after day, and it became tradition: wait until the others trickled out after practice, one by one, and then let Maria press me up against the full-length mirrors and kiss me breathless. Or sit by her on the floor, hand in hand, and talk about a future so close we could see the whites of its eyes. Or just be silent, in each other's arms.

The first time I brought Maria home with me was also the first time I ever showed someone else my box. She watched it with bright eyes, watched the doll turning around and around, and I didn't have the courage to tell her that she was the doll. That I had wanted it to be me, but it was her, that perfect figure with shoes laced all the way up.

I knew more about Maria than I had known about most anyone. I knew the curves of her mouth and the smile she gave so rarely that its appearance was a gift in and of itself. I knew that she had troubles with eating, with weight — most of us did, and I was no exception.

The difference was that I didn't faint for lack of calories in the middle of what was supposed to be an unimportant showcase.

It was hard for Maria, and therefore hard on me. She tried to beat the compulsions. Somehow, though, she could never see the Maria I saw. I was Clara in the *Nutcracker*, but I couldn't get her out of my head the whole time. How could I fall in love with a magician's nephew when Maria was there, Maria existed?

I watched the dancer in my box, and wondered if she was too skinny. It was the first time I'd thought that doll could be anything but perfect.

They kicked Maria out of school, and she asked me to come with her.

She knew it was selfish, and I knew it was selfish, but she still screamed at me when I said no. That's what I remember before she left, though I try to hold on to the sweet kisses and practice room talks. I try to see her smile and instead I hear the fight.

Afterwards, when I was walking home alone, I wondered if I had any of her clothes still at my apartment. I did — a shirt, light blue. It smelled like her. I held it as I listened to my music box — somehow I knew, even then, that I wouldn't see her again. I looked at the box with watery eyes, at the roses whose color had all but entirely flaked away.

As I reached out to close the music box, I nudged it a bit too far off the edge of my nightstand. I saw it fall, knew I couldn't stop it. The song, so familiar, played even as it fell, tilted face downward, towards the ground.

As it turned out, the doll was porcelain, after all.

Shut

by Erin Samantha Hanson

2020 Scholarship Winner

I think that the first time that I thought I knew love was when a girl with bright red hair held my head underwater.
Her teeth were like broken steak knives, and all I could think was that I wanted to kiss her.
Every time she looked at me, it was like she was putting cigarettes out on my skin
and that's only a metaphor for my unrequited love because something in me believes that my kind of love is all danger and pain and masochism.
She tells me that she hates me
That everyone hates me.

I'm drowning.
My head is under water, but I don't think that it's because she's holding it down anymore.
My last gasping breaths float to the surface in the form of bubbles and everyone sits around, watching in awe and popping each one.

Every girl I've ever loved I've treated like a piece of fiction.
And if fiction has taught me anything, it's that my stories end in blood and violence and pain.
So maybe it's some sadistic, honest part of me that only loves girls who can ruin me.
Because if this is going to be a realistic piece of fiction, it has to hurt.
It has to end in tragedy.

I realize that I'm in love with a girl who trusts me completely
and I suddenly feel like a wolf backing her into a corner.
I'm a predatory animal and now I'm the one with knives for teeth.

The girl with bright red hair only loves boys.
Suddenly the whole story is different, and sure, she was holding my head underwater, but only because I wanted to touch her lips with my fingertips.
And I'm drowning.
I am drowning
But I've wanted to kiss girls since I was twelve and that means that I'm dead already.

I fall in love with a helpless child and suddenly the world forgets that I'm a child too.
I'm a predatory animal
But the men who touch me where I don't want them to are only doing what's natural.
I have long understood that I am a little girl when I'm angry and a woman when you rape me.
Girls who think about kissing girls are dead unless they keep their mouths shut.

I get a phone call when I'm fifteen.
No caller ID.
I'm out with my friends. It's a Saturday night and I'm having fun.
I answer the call and I hear my name mixed with a series of slurs and obscenities.
I snarl and I bare my teeth, because what the hell is the point of being a dangerous animal if I don't even get a growl.
And I hang up.
And I get five more calls.
I let my phone buzz on the table of the coffee shop, but I don't cry, because I've cried before, and it never makes the world any softer.
The next day I tell my friends not to tell anyone about me.
Because a girl who thinks about kissing other girls is dead unless she keeps her mouth shut.

People shove me against lockers in the hallway.
I ask my friends if it's that obvious.
And they laugh and tell me yes.
They don't understand how terrifying that answer is.

I think that I like writing poetry because it feels like love.
Not because it's beautiful. But no punctuation. No boundaries.
My mother is supportive, but in the way that it's fine as long as who I am is nothing more than a bad pun or a tragic story.
My existence in an honest and nonconventional way is so unacceptable.
It's fine as long as I fit within the little box that people who have never had these kinds of experiences have made for me.
It's fine as long as I understand and accept the consequences.
It's fine as long as I don't shove it in your face.
It's fine as long as I stay away from your daughter.
It's fine as long as I don't have a crush on you.
It's fine as long as I keep my mouth shut.

People say that they like me as long as they can ignore my gayness
Like it is a separate part of me.
Like it is not woven into the very fabric of who I am.
Molotov cocktails and your daughter's soft palms, I have two hands.
We kiss and her lips are touching scar tissue.
My queerness is a real, breathing thing that does not disappear when there is no love.
I have spent so long in rooms void of love and my queerness is there, stark and ugly.
It is not your split lip.
Only a faint scar when it is away from the sharp edge that split it.
It is pneumonia.
It is a painful, crackling thing that lives inside of my lungs.

It is the hurt and the discomfort that makes me painfully aware of my lungs and where they are in my body in a way that my other organs do not.
Run your tongue across your teeth.
Count them.
Aren't there too many?
Too many, too many.
Pull them out.

The world is holding my head underwater and I'm drowning, I can't breathe.
I've never wondered what it was like to like boys.
But now I'm drowning and my ears are ringing and I dare to think that maybe if you all want to paint me as an animal, then the next time that you lay your hands on me, I'll tear you apart with my teeth.
My head's underwater and I'm drowning and some soft, tender part of me wonders what it's like to kiss someone and not scrub your body until it bleeds just to feel clean.
I wonder if that's what that gay kid one town over from where I grew up thought as he was waterboarded in the high school locker room by the boys' wrestling team.
Maybe he would've been fine if he had just kept his mouth shut.

They're not holding my head underwater because my sexuality makes me feel like I'm drowning, hollow and scared and numb.
They're holding my head under water because they are trying to kill me.

The first time that I thought I knew love, it was because the world had taught me that it was a perfect image of what my love is supposed to look like.
They're holding my head underwater, and you're all crying because it's so sad.
I'm just another tragic story (Melania Geymonat, Christine Hannigan), another statistic (one in five LGBT people have experienced a hate crime due to their sexual orientation in the last twelve months).
You're crying

And they're holding my head underwater
And you just watch.
I guess that I should have kept my mouth shut.

Those Summer Nights

by Anonymous

The whir of bike tires against the paled concrete droned through the hot summer air. Hot rapid breaths synced with the nearly audible thrum of a pounding heart. *Click, click, click!* The gears adjusted to accommodate the steep dips and progressively rougher texture of the road.

Harsh radio static cut through the ambient noises, nearly sending the cruising bike off its course. A loud voice finally broke through, "Hey! I'm 20 minutes out. What about you, Angie?"

An unsteady hand blindly fumbled through the contents of the attached basket. Finally, it closed around a large block of plastic tucked beneath a bundled blanket. With the swift flick of a wrist, the antenna was extended and the side button was pressed.

After taking a moment to steady heaving breaths, "About 30 minutes, over." The static returned.

"'Over,' real cute."

"It's what the pros do." A wheeze followed the quick succession of words. The walkie-talkie was haphazardly tossed back into the basket, the bike was once again steadied with the addition of the second hand. Gasps and wheezes disrupted the static, and finally, a strained voice came through.

"Five minutes, over," a deep voice gasped. Cackles rang out from the speaker.

"Ralph, you sound like y'gonna have a heart attack!" The cackles devolved into hysteric laughter and gasps for breath.

Angela groaned in annoyance, reaching back into the basket to muffle the walkie-talkie with the blanket. She directed her attention back to the road and then toward the sky. The sun still shone amidst the watery oranges and pinks that swirled around it.

***

Bzzzz. Thawp! Another mosquito splattered across a beet-red cheek.

"Gross," an exasperated voice cried, followed by a sweaty palm quickly scrubbing at the remnants.

Jamie oftentimes referred to themself as a tree-hugger. But they never quite made peace with the more invasive insects. Nevertheless, that didn't prevent guilt from blossoming in their chest when unlucky bugs were flatted by their palm. Exasperated with the nerve-wracking hum of the mosquitos and flies, Jamie slung their knapsack on the damp woodland floor and flipped the flap over to carefully rummage through the neatly organized contents. With the click of a button, loud static jumped to life.

"Anyone close to the clubhouse?" Jamie called into the walkie-talkie, frustratingly flinging their hand to swat at incoming flies.

Soft crackles broke through the static. Multiple voices rang out, calling out different times and bits of conversation. Jamie pinched the bridge of their nose, mentally mapping out where everyone was before pressing the walkie-talkie against their lips again.

"See you soon then, Ralph. Everyone else hurry up."

The walkie-talkie was packed back into the knapsack before Jamie awkwardly clambered up the cool rungs of a ladder screwed into a large oak tree. The overfilled bag barely fit through the small opening above the ladder. It was carefully slipped off and thrown into the treehouse above. Jamie heaved themself in after it, quickly closing the hatch. They sighed in relief, the heat and the insects now blocked out.

The room was considerably large for a treehouse. A full-sized door led out to a small deck that overlooked the fireplace below. Four bean bags were lining the walls of the room, each color corresponding to a member. Jamie stared at the stained wood boards that made up the walls. As Jamie's eyes traveled along the grain, their mind wandered to the memories of the summer that their dad spent lovingly piecing together the treehouse. They would watch happily as he firmly secured the ladder to the thick trunk of the tree; it was a final touch. He puffed out a long sigh as he inspected it. He finally turned to grin at Jamie. It was their piece of heaven, nestled well into in the wilderness surrounding their ranch house.

Jamie thought back to the day they had invited their friends to the treehouse. The plastic landline clutched in Jamie's hand could barely handle the overlapping cheers and excited voices. It soon became a cherished tradition amongst the group. Their summer nights were spent curled up by a roaring fire or listening to the summer showers tap against the roof of the treehouse. Roasted marshmallows would stick to their fingers and chins. The ghosts of laughter and jovial conversation would dissipate into the air, swirling upwards with the smoke of the smoldering fire. It was their haven. For when they were cast aside by their small town for who they were, they found acceptance and love within each other, within that small stretch of land.

Heavy knocks at the closed hatch snapped Jamie from their thoughts. The hatch flew open before they had the chance to pull it open. Ralph's head poked through the opening, his face flushed and glistening from sweat.

"Hey," he gasped, throwing in his bag and hopping inside.

"Hi," Jamie chirped.

Ralph glanced around the room and his eyes finally settled on a green bean bag, which he happily sank into with his bag at his feet.

"You good?" Jamie asked.

Ralph nodded but his heaving chest and pants said otherwise. "I brought the marshmallows." He paused to open his bag and pull out a plastic bag full of marshmallows. "They're a little banged up though."

Jamie dismissively waved their hand. "Don't worry about it. Can you help me get the fire pit going?"

Ralph groaned and begrudgingly rose from the bean bag. "Why can't Sky help you do that?"

Jamie opened the hatch and slipped out of the treehouse. Ralph followed suit as Jamie explained, "I want to get it done now and she won't be here for a while."

"I just sat down," Ralph muttered under his breath.

The previous night's rain made it difficult to find dry brush. Nonetheless, the two of them scrounged together a decent sized pile of dry levels and twigs in the center of a designated ring of stones. Jamie grumbled curses when Ralph admitted he had forgotten his lighter in his backpack in his haste.

Finally, they both managed to nurse a small flame within the brush. Jamie skillfully fed it and blew it into a roaring fire. Ralph, who was much too scared of the flame's heat, simply sat on a nearby log and watched with awe in his eyes. Jamie stepped back to admire the fruits of their efforts: a cracking, hungry flame. Satisfied, they plopped onto the log beside Ralph.

Side by side, they shared a moment of peace. The air danced with gentle heat and the hushed crackle of leaves, but the steady thrum of the woods kept its dance slow.

Ralph's eyes became heavy and his heart settled deep within his chest. His thoughts wandered to those summers when the air was much like this. It would be thick, but it readily embraced him with its warmth. And trees would hum lullabies of times long past. And his head would be cradled in the lap of a love long lost. And he too would join the trees in their melody, watching his twinkling eyes as Ralph's own fluttered shut.

"Hey, assholes!" A squeal tore Ralph from his reminisces. From his side, he could hear Jamie groan in annoyance. His gaze flickered toward a pair of figures that seemed to fly across the dirt path. They were traveling so fast that he had to leap from his seat to avoid their skidding bikes.

"Don't do that!" he cried out, flailing his arms at the new arrivals.

"You could've gone into the fire pit," Jamie added.

Skylar ignored their scolding; she simply tossed her helmet onto the ground alongside her bike. She made quick work of tugging her long dirty blonde hair back into a ponytail.

But Angela's red face scrunched in shame. "Sorry guys."

"It's okay," Jamie muttered.

Before Angela could reach for the latch on the strap of her helmet, Skylar had already been fumbling for it. She clumsily pulled the helmet from her head and discarded it alongside her own.

"Thanks," Angela mumbled, a small smile tugging at the corner of her lips.

"No problem, babe," Skylar said, pulling the taller girl down to her level to sloppily kiss her.

Ralph feigned to dry heave. "Oh, get a room!"

"We'll take the treehouse," Skylar quipped.

The group silently hurried to prepare all that they needed for the night. Skylar put together a plate of Ralph's partially melted marshmallows speared on sticks with graham cracks and chocolate bars. She snuck small chunks of chocolate when no one was looking, sometimes slipping some to a busied Angela. Angela eventually began scolding Skylar so that she could focus on diligently organizing sleeping bags in the treehouse. Below, Ralph lit bug repellent candles around the fire pit site. Jamie chose the simplest task, cleaning off the logs that were placed around the fire.

Ralph called up to the girls once he was sure he and Jamie had finished. "Sky! Angie! You done?"

Skylar's face appeared in the window and she pressed a thumbs-up beside it.

Ralph called back up, "Then come down here!"

Soon the four of them were gathered around the roaring fire. The night had enveloped the cold woods around them. But the warmth of their blankets and each other brought comfort in the dry dark. Their merry voices mingled with the chirps of the creatures of the night. The plate of marshmallows was passed amongst them. The orange flames of the fire licked at the treat, crisping the outside.

Skylar tucked herself under Angela's arm, nestling into the soft fabric of her shirt. Ralph gazed at the stars, happily chewing at the gooey marshmallow in his mouth. And Jamie looked at the soft smiles of contentment on their friends' faces, and they too found themself smiling.

Those summer nights when the sun extinguished on the horizon, the nights when the hum of insects and the chirp of the crickets would lull tired souls to a rest full of dreams, those were the nights that the rolling waves of time would never wash away.

Her

by Devi Patel

I stare into her eyes,
They scream of how tired she is,
Hung with dark bags and lines.
Obscurely depicting the seldom excitement she wishes to feign.
The gateways to the soul are blackened underneath pounds of pressure,
Wanting to elude from Van Gough,
To appear more real, whilst not being as such.
Adorned by decorative lashes and bright colors,
I admire her beauty.
The painted brush strokes of elegance and class,
Fights to be the press,
To share the most outrageous story,
To elevate her status.
She chooses not what is put on her, yet, fights not to deny acceptance of the narrative.
I wish to reach out and feel her hands,
Rough with too much texture,
Sandpaper wounds that do not compare to the scars buried underneath years of layers.
She wishes to one day to be able to provide a mother's touch,
To comfort her kin with such love and adoration,
But knows her hands will only cause paper cuts,
Reminding burns, hurting the nerves without permanent damage.

Standing taut, staring boredly into the eyes of the social structure before her,
She is strong enough to keep her mind alive,
Yet lacks the strength to break the chains that the world has locked onto her ankles.
Matted silver cuffs hang tightly around neck,
Leading her as if though she was a disobedient dog,

Trapped, being dragged by her leader who only speaks in foreign language.
She locks hands with the masculine plastic doll across from her stance,
She is completely adored in white lace and artistic embroidery,
She's making a deal to give up her soul, in return wanting to receive stability.
A fake reality in order to avoid discrepancies,
To convince all others that she is pure,
To belt that she is the same as the rest of the toys.
They speak their contractual vows,
Promising promises they both wish someone else besides their opposite was actually promising.
As every plastic words falls from her mouth,
The keys of the piano key louder in my head,
As if an instinctual siren is warning me that if I continue to listen to these screams,
I will fall down upon my knees,
Scraping the skin, reminding me,
Of where I should actually be,
Not on the sidelines watching the lady in white, with the prison cabins wrapped around her chest,
But instead in the arms of my lady with the colorful eyes,
Mindset in our happy reality,
Where no one can tell us who or what we can or cannot be.
In a world where I love her and she loves me.

"I do."
"I do."
I fall upon my knees,
Because in this world,
Hate will always prevent love from creating a stir,
She cannot be with me,
And I cannot be with
Her.

How the Memory of a Curry Bowl Healed Me

by Xinyi L.

Content warning: disordered eating

Wow … Mom's curry laksa smells amazing, I think to myself. The sweet, subtle aroma of coconut milk, the citrus from the green kaffir lime, and the pungent, tingling spice from the chilies bring me back to my hometown in Malaysia. I am flooded with memories of exquisite pastry shops hidden behind old cobblestone alleyways, joyous meals savored at loud food courts with massive ceiling fans, and adventures hunting for irresistible street food at Pasar Malam night markets. *But you cannot have it,* I tell myself as I snap back to reality. *Don't do it. You know why.*

The demons in my head raise their voices until I am aware of nothing but their tormenting screams. In a few seconds, my favorite childhood dish —one that had never failed to bring a smile to my face as a little kid — is reduced to mere concepts of "good" or "bad," of "can have" or "cannot have," of numbers and calories and macros and micros. My thoughts ricochet through my body and beat down upon me until I can no longer breathe, until I can no longer see through my tears. My knees buckle, weak from mental and physical exhaustion, and I fall to the ground, hugging myself as I cry.

"I'm sorry. I'm sorry. I'm sorry," I repeat. Tens, hundreds of times. Then, on trembling legs, I force myself to rise. With shaky hands and newfound purpose, I scoop out the greatest portion of curry laksa the world has ever seen.

Throughout this same world, people celebrate food for the history it entails, the bright cultures it shares, and the personal stories it unravels. However, food is an uncomfortable subject for many struggling transgender individuals.

When I looked at my body, I felt only deep hatred. My body carried extra weight in areas that did not define me, extra weight on my chest and my hips. My body dysmorphia exaggerated these features to the point where I felt sick looking in the mirror. Because of this, I progressively lost my appetite and had difficulty eating my meals. At first, I feared for my health because of how little I was consuming. But soon, I saw the changes in my body. My chest had gotten smaller, my hips narrower, and I had a boxier physique in general. I became obsessed with the results and made my goal to lose as much of the problem areas as possible. Relatives started to ask if I was okay and started commenting that I looked like a skeleton — but I did not care. I loved the feeling of a lanky body with minimal curves; my gender dysphoria adored the boyish figure. I believed things were finally going right, until one day everything went wrong, and I collapsed on the hard concrete floor.

I knew living beings needed food to fuel their functioning bodies and experience beautiful moments with friends and family. I knew this in theory, but food still became an enemy. No matter how hard I tried, I could not find a balance between a healthy body and healthy mind. In moments my body was healthy, my brain drowned in self-hatred. Likewise, during times my brain was happy, my body struggled. I was stuck in an infinite cycle of guilt and hatred.

Then one night, I decided I was done feeling trapped. I asked myself why it seemed that no matter what I did, I could never escape the cycle and find happiness.

My brain then led me to memories of a time I was happy, a time when I was a child, young and carefree. Food would always bring me happiness. Why was it different now?

Having a boyish figure made the torments of my dysphoria quieter for sure, but I never felt good. I worried nonstop that I would "revert" to my old body if I allowed myself more food, even if my stomach screamed to be fed. I was constantly weak, cold, and irritable. I soon realized that my new body did not reflect the strong, passionate man on the inside. I was frail enough to be broken by the wind and had no energy left to chase my dreams.

Slowly, I learned that being comfortable in my body meant feeling good and feeling strong, not just looking a certain way in the mirror. That night, I drifted to sleep with a changed perspective on food and an understanding of the importance of health to live a fulfilling life.

The next morning, I ate my grand portion of curry laksa with tears running down my cheeks, fearful but resolved. My body yearned to run away and burn off the calories on the family treadmill; my pair of wooden chopsticks flew out of my shaky hands. My entire body fought against me as I consumed the decadent bowl of noodles. The voices in my head called me worthless, weak, and a disappointment, but I had set my intentions and knew that I would accomplish it. So I relished the bowl in front of me, the heavenly combination of springy noodles, silky coconut broth, fragrant spices, fresh herbs, and bittersweet sour kaffir lime, with no apology.

For the first time since I fell victim to my eating disorder, I felt a spark of hope. I honored the little kid in me again, the one that always had a smile on their face as they ate their favorite curry laksa dish. I turned to food to heal my body and my mind, cherishing its exploding textures and the sweet, salty, spicy, sour, and umami sensations that flooded my taste buds with every bite. I thrived on the freedom and energy food brought me. I could finally go on runs again, share ice cream with my friends on sweltering summer days, and no longer had to worry about passing out in the middle of class. Part of me was hesitant to believe, but the torments of my gender dysphoria slowly lessened and I could enjoy life without obsessing over my appearance. If I was sure about one thing, it was that food was a friend and not an enemy.

Eating disorders are an issue still clouded with uncertainty, loneliness, and isolation, especially in the transgender community. In many countries, including my hometown of Malaysia, both subjects are taboo. There is a constant pressure for transgender individuals to feel and look like the "typical" image of gender portrayed by society. Sometimes, the desire to meet this standard manifests in ways that harm us. I started off making a few changes to my daily routine, thinking it would not hurt me, and ended with a debilitating eating disorder. I know now that depriving my body of food was not the right path to take, but there are many individuals, both young and old, that struggle to understand this. For this reason, I share my story and hope others will hear my voice.

There are irreplaceable moments only food can bring, like sipping on hot cups of tea on a rainy day with a good book, learning my grandmother's famous banana bread recipe, or experiencing cultures through exquisite plates of food only found in a foreign country. I realized that I needed my body to be healthy to experience not just another bowl of curry but the transitioned life waiting for me.

These days, I accept who I am. Taking better care of my body transformed my mind into a more understanding place. The voices are quieter, and though I still have much to work on, I take pride in how far I have come. I remind myself of my goal to one day have a healthy transitioned body and advocate for those in the same situation. Therefore, I treat myself with love and care so that my pre-transition body and mind live to see the day they fulfill their dream.

Sleepover

by Mackenzie Acree

I remember being eleven.
Sam's mom always makes her wear dresses on Sundays
Which she hates
(because dresses are the devil),
And she lives in cargo shorts with her hair pulled back.
She is my best friend.
She is dyslexic, and I help her with her homework every day.
She has a beautiful voice.

I am almost twelve,
And Sam is the prettiest girl I have ever seen.
She goes to a different school now,
But we have sleepovers with our friends almost every weekend
And play games well into the night.
She loves Taylor Swift and roller-skating,
And when the other girls dare her to kiss me,
She only hesitates for a second.

I am now twelve,
And I have sworn off boys
(because they suck, obviously).
It is Saturday night,
And we have just finished a *Twilight* marathon.
We sit up in my bed with the lights off,
And I ask if I can kiss her.
I am terrified when she says yes.
Her lips are softer than mine,
And her hand is warm where it rests against my neck.
She does not kiss like a boy.

I am almost thirteen,
And Sam has a boyfriend.
I cry in my art class and paint something with flowers on it.
She does not call me for sleepovers anymore,
So I find a new best friend.
Eventually, I find a boyfriend too.
I do not speak to her again.

Addendum:
I am almost fourteen,
And Elizabeth's parents are … pagans?
They let me spend the night,
And in the morning her mom makes the best scrambled eggs I have ever had.
She holds my hand in the hallway
And yells at the boy who calls us dykes in gym class.
I think I love her.
Maybe I do.

Vertigo

by Layla Felder

falling
the vertigo should've been a sign
a heady feeling
giddy in its novelty
soon souring as
uncertainty began to roil in my stomach
at first only a mild discomfort
but turning to pain as it became turmoil and rose in my throat like bile
but I didn't get down
didn't step back
didn't listen
i thought it was simple
i thought i was invincible
and now here i was
falling like Alice
desperate to reach Wonderland
but stuck in the fall down the hole
arms blown back
the stinging wind raking at my eyes
bringing tears.
i'd tripped you see.
tripped on a black stiletto
attached to an elegantly stretched leg
the waves of her hips cresting and sliding into the curves of her chest
a murmuring ocean
lips the color of ripe peaches
eyes dark
beckoning
bottomless

and i fell in

hands a frenzy on my iPhone keyboard
clicking yes
no
blue
once
on every 'am i gay'
'am i bi'
'how to know if you're queer' quiz
Buzzed had to offer
next to YouTube
girls with short bobs
pink hair
guys with expressive hands
watching mouths move
taking in sounds
how each
'self-discovery'
'how i found out i was gay'
'my first realization' story
compared to my own
panicking at the lack of similarity

brain overheating like an overworked computer
buckling under the duress
the stress
of feeling these feelings
the butterflies
the racing heart
the throbbing body
and having no explanation

no x= for the equation of my sexuality
an equation i hadn't even known existed

as a child marriage rights
discrimination
homophobia
had always set my blood aflame
brought forth angry tears
at the unfairness and injustice
and rendered me speechless for the question
"why are you so angry?"
i'd always felt feelings for both sexes
but only the boys were 'crushes'
i'd been taught that girls were 'girl crushes'
admiration of the beauty of women not to be taken as serious emotional connection

but here i was
years later
feeling not only admiration but
adoration
infatuation
passion
longing
and desire

where before my fall had been tentative
cautious
unsure
i now fell with a hopeless permanence
each day consumed by the unknown
the fear of what i might be

locked in battle with
my hope that i might be what i fear i am
Adam and Eve each offered me apples and i took both
now the snake had wrapped itself around my neck
squeezing until i couldn't breathe
whispering with malice that
i was a liar
a fake
a cheat
dramatic
attention seeking
desperate
wrong
bad
condemned to a hell of my own creation
as my face turned blue i closed my eyes
let my arms be buffeted by the wind
oblivious to the melting of hot night to hotter day as i continued to fall
watching the tunnel turn from earthy brown to grey to black
color seeping from the world
like a picture submerged in water
face muscles atrophying
forgetting what it is to smile

but then a woman appeared
floating parallel to me
she uncoiled the snake from my throat
and gently touched my red, raw skin
her smooth, cool hands like a balm to my inflamed flesh
her eyes took me in
soft and gentle
with a gaze like warm honey.

my eyes filled as relief flooded my body like morphine

and then I hit the ground

For Girls Like Me

by Katelyn Michelle Buck

"I think that's Ursa Major, and that one is Orion. Corvus is hiding behind that roof — over there." I lifted a finger to gesture to the black-tiled roof that seemed to blend together with the night. Party lights dimmed and music faded where I sat; I could see my breath linger in the air after speaking. There was a boy to my left — I had never talked to him much in school. He had on clothes that I couldn't describe because night fell so quickly. He played basketball, I knew that; he played basketball and he was popular. He wasn't the usual type of person I talk to, but just for tonight, I thought, Popular Boy would be my best friend. He would be my best friend, and he would listen to me point out stars that I hadn't searched for in so, so long. The stars and him became my distraction that night. Though, maybe he thought the same about me, because he never left.

Every Monday night Mom and I watched *The Bachelor* — a sacred tradition. I think that's where my obsession with romance started — Mom's Monday night *Bachelor* watch parties; or maybe it was the Disney channel movies that had such tender love stories that would make anyone envy the gorgeous female lead and her fantastical romantic ventures. Grand, romantic escapades utterly entranced me.

I developed this yearning for the elegant fantasy of love. It became my ultimate dream, a great love story always seemed to solve that which hands could not touch. I would stare into the sky, studying the stars for a wish, praying for a grand romance. It was meant for me — I knew it. And as I watched the stars shine and dim, I thought about how I would draw my story up there someday. I thought the greatest love stories were always written in the stars.

My dad bought me a telescope when I was a kid — in the years before he left. So often, he would focus on a star, and I would be too scared to look for another one because I didn't want to lose the one I already had. I couldn't imagine never being able to find it again. I would look at it for long whiles, and I would believe my dad when he told me it's a planet far, far away from us. Venus. He told me I could always find her because she was always the brightest star in the sky. I don't know how he could have known so much about the stars, but I believed him. I believed in a lot of things then. I believed in magic and the stars knowing my name, in the tales I dreamed up in my head of the grand romances I would have, and in someone waiting for me out there — somewhere.

I came up with this idea that the stars always had something to tell me — that my past, present, and future waited up there, holding its hand out to me like it was waiting for me to come home. A wild magic always followed me when I would find Venus again. I envisioned ribbons of pinks and purples and blues dancing around me to the rhythm of a wedding song as I watched her glow. Venus was the only part of the night's sky that never intimidated me.

Though, as I grew, I looked away from the stars more and more, avoiding what was once my solace. Maybe I was afraid of looking up at them and remembering my dad, or maybe I was more afraid of seeing something I didn't want to be there. There were so many stars and millions of possible bad endings to my story. Maybe the stars started becoming scary after he left. Maybe it's other people that make the infinite bearable.

By middle school, my dad was long gone, and I stopped watching *The Bachelor* with my mom, but I still thought about love every day of the week. I thought about what it meant: Was it a promise? Was it an answer? Was it an inevitability? Surely, I thought, the last one has to be true. I wanted it so bad; I craved to love and to be loved. It was the only thing I was sure of: I would have a great love story, and it would make everything else okay. Because love is this wild, magical thing. It is the stars whispering your name in the ear of someone else. It's the ache in your chest of knowing they're waiting for you out there in the mysterious future. It's the warmth in your soul of knowing you won't be alone forever, that someone will find you and you'll survive together.

Except, the days passed on and I felt an insufferable, attractionless yearning grow and grow in my body until I was consuming any tale of romance that I could get my hands on to settle my soul.

In seventh grade, I learned what being queer meant, and I felt a connection to the word. I knew my answers were somewhere connected to this community. And then, I discovered asexuality, and all of the dreams and fantasies I had in my head of a life full of romance and sweethearts and stars vanished painfully. Each dream I had was falling apart like a growing crack in the mother earth. I watched my world begin to crumble.

Asexuality came unwelcomed. It definitely made sense; I had an answer for who I was and why I felt the way I did. Yet, I soon started a long, groaning period of denial. I still idealized this life in my head of love and romance. When I discovered that romance and sexuality were separate identities, I deluded myself into believing I felt romantic attraction. I had to. I held on so tight to those fantasies that letting go felt like plunging down into a deep, dark unknown. A life without those dreams was foreign and so, so terrifying — more terrifying than anything I had ever felt before.

I tortured myself by denying my aromanticism. Pain found its place in my chest, swirling around my heart and mixing with anxiety and desperation. I felt sick often. High school came and I manufactured what I thought attraction was. I picked schoolmates who I thought were attractive by all the right definitions and told myself that this is what being in love was: looking at Bryce Henderson from across the classroom and pretending that "cute dimples" and "nice hair" made me feel something. I thought, this is what I wanted. I told myself that, sometimes, love took a little work — that my dream was still waiting for me. And yet, I never dated.

I think some part of me knew what I was doing to myself was naive and pointless. It was a part of me that I never acknowledged — the part of me that I avoided constantly. With each day that I led myself to believe in romantic fairy tales, I felt sadness curdle and twist in my chest, and it spread to my arms, legs, and brain until it took over all of me. I thought that this hurt, this painful yearning for a promise never meant for me, would be less horrifying than what lies behind the truth. It was less scary to hurt than to plunge into an unknown reality where the rules on what life was weren't so easy. Abandoning my childlike visions of romantic love, it was like losing focus on the star I already had.

Then, my friend had a party, and I found myself next to Popular Boy —noticing for the first time how lonely he seemed. He had dark skin and dark hair and he was never anything but wholeheartedly joyful. He was quiet then. He wasn't the type of person I usually talk to — I'm not the jock type. Except, high school prestige didn't seem to matter anymore in the smoke of a bonfire outside that spoke the language of youth and with the spice of pork tamales still lingering on our tongues. Our limbs hung heavy with exhaustion from dancing and our clothes smelled of hearth and all that mattered was to share this moment between both of us — the secret stars that no one else had noticed shining brighter at the side of the yard. I didn't know his story, and he didn't know mine. But that meant nothing anymore; all we cared about was what constellations I could look up on my phone and where we could find them.

We sat in old patio furniture that had been abandoned in the hidden parts of the backyard, where I committed a type of wild abandonment of all my anxieties and terrors. I pointed out Corvus, Ursa Major, Orion, and a few other constellations that seemed less important in the moment compared to the euphoria I felt rush through me — because, I was smiling at the stars again. And they were smiling back, winding their way through the sky to tell me stories like they always used to. I tried to find Venus again; I couldn't. Maybe she was gone, or maybe her shine was the same as every other star swimming in the sky. I guess she didn't matter anymore, either. Nothing mattered then except the stars and the freedom I had for just one night.

Almost a year has passed since then, and I'm still not sure what to make of that night. It was beautiful, but not in the easy way. It was beautiful in the way that there is no other word to describe it. It was a beautiful night for how free I felt, how I let go of the anxiety I felt about love, how a child's dream to be a stunning bride seemed further away than it ever did before.

Months passed and slowly love, once a dream and a vision, turned into a passive thing. It didn't seem as big and imposing as it always had. It was as if I could look at it and understand it logically, but emotionally, romance was something that would never connect with me.

Aromanticism, after that night, seemed less scary than it had before. I still feel loss at the crumbling of the fantasies I nurtured all my life. And yet, now I create new dreams. A life without sexual or romantic attraction — my full and passionate life — will grow and I will embrace it wildly. It will foster love — all of the various types that matter. I will grow, and I will find more stories in the stars. Perhaps, I will write some stories of my own, stories of girls like me, but one who could find magic in the palm of her hand before she found it in another person.

A love grows in my heart still: a romance non-exclusive. I feel it deep in my bones to my soul and to the roots of my feet digging into the earth; it's the warmth of a hug from my mother, the adrenaline of glee I get from my friends, the stinging tears of hurt contrasting the comfort from the embrace of my best friend. I have a romance with myself. It is a lifelong partnership that I hadn't seen coming, but I now know it was inevitable. The love I feel for my family, friends, and self is no less important than the love felt by the married strangers on the street.

I have a love for the stars, continuously, as well. I still wonder, in awe, at the stories they weave for me in the night. I still imagine the tendrils of pinks and purples and blues that dance, now, to the rhythm of my own melody. They show me the path to my own story, one that doesn't exist yet on my bookshelf of grand romances. My story will, indeed, be one of love, not the type I had always envisioned, but nonetheless just as important — and just as magical.

Stereotypes

by Raiyne Brant

Stereotypes were
Always funny to me.
The idea that a group
Would fall under the same
Ideas and likes.
That was,
Until I realized
I followed
Asexual stereotypes.

Obsessed with dragons?
Check.
Rather cake over humans?
Check.
Loves space?
Check.
Way too many puns?
Check.

Maybe people
Just try to conform
To their given stereotypes
Or the stereotypes are true.
Whatever it is,
I don't mind
Because it feels
As though
I actually belong.

Beetles

by Haven Hitchcock

In the beginning every second was devoted to
Keeping a secret.
I made myself rules —
Password protected diaries,
Smile through the longing,
Tears were only allowed past 11pm in the dark.
Secrets fill up my body like
Black beetles.
Too ugly to be seen,
They stabbed my insides but
I caged them within,
Built up a staggering wall between me and others.

When my secret was freed and let in the open air,
All the wrong people knew and somehow the
Lies grew.
They swelled and took up my oxygen supply,
Breaths became gasps,
Choking on blank space,
Bringing the empty inside me.
Hidden-for-too-long secrets became strewn about
Like dirty clothes in too-messy bedrooms when any energy
Meant for cleaning was thrust into keeping up appearances.

Freedom in truth is a bittersweet thing.
Every word I spoke was a falsehood because I couldn't handle the judgement.
And even now,
Instinctively I keep us quiet.
I don't hold hands with you in the hallways,
I bring friends with us to the mall,

To my grandparents and strangers, you are "my … friend …"
No
One
Should
Know.
They see me as a woman and I cannot correct them,
And you, with your long hair, you are a woman too.

My exoskeleton keeps out hurt but traps it inside, too.
Juicy sincere insides are crushed but
Contained.
Millions of beetles spill from my mouth, eyes, and hands
Too quick for me to stuff back inside.
And I see the looks I get,
I hear the whispers.
You should learn from my silence,
From my patience.
I wait for when I can love with eyes,
Ears
And
Hands
Open.

Pronounless poetry flows out full of verses about a love too deep for words
Singular syllables short and sweet stumble and struggle for some air,
No!
Don't share anything too real or really revealing.
Human guts weren't made to be seen, right?
No one wants raw and bloody and purply bruised,
Full of numb nerves innumerable in their utter neutrality.

I sit and think and I am quiet outside,

A person shrouded in silence falling back into old habits.
And I let myself think just for an instant —
Maybe someday I'll be beautiful inside too.

Take me in your gentle hands and
Hold me.
Send spilt blood back inside,
Pull the gauze from my mouth,
Stitch my lungs back together,
Fix Me.
Because I'm not sure I know how.
Crush the bugs crawling around inside me,
Please.

The truth opened a door to new kinds of achings.
Glitter and gold glisten like grown in graces,
Taunting with a mercy I'm still waiting for.
I'll keep one beetle as a memory,
One single shard of a shredded story,
A perfect piece that pulls to view an imperfect past.
There's a time and place for love,
So I'll wait until then.

We Have Not Touched the Stars

by Anonymous

Whoever said they could be "bounded in a nutshell" and count themself "a king of infinite space" had never been on a spaceship. Take it from me. I've never been off a spaceship.

The world of a spaceship is made of machinery, fringed by borders marked with astro-glass. There is a definite up and down (thanks, generated gravity), but this is largely secondary to the most important dichotomy: in and out, rendered distinct only by three feet of metal and a sealed airlock. The most comparable experience may be looking out of an aquarium at an utterly alien world you are always aware would gladly consume you whole. Despite this, the ship is still comforting if it is all you know.

They built this ship to be a home.

I think there has to be some love in that.

It has twists and corners and secrets, a place for generations of the community to grow up together. This was by design.

The first people to board the ARK, the (allegorically apt) generation ship on a four-lightyear journey to the exoplanets of the Alpha Centauri System, were our parents.

I don't know yet if I forgive them.

***

"We tried the world. Good god, it wasn't for us," says my mother when I ask her about Earth. It feels like a quote, by the rhythm she uses, or a plea. An old memory.

My mom and the others made the choice to board this ship, sentenced themselves and their children to a life in steel walls. It's been a long time since then. Folks didn't start popping babies out immediately upon exiting orbit, so there's actually more of a delay than you'd think between the Terrans and the second generation. The Terrans were largely adults when they boarded, but the closed gene-pool meant the starting set only had so many potential generations before they had to break out the artificial insemination samples. As such, the space-born generation was delayed as long as possible before concerns for cultural erosion became relevant. It's been a lifetime for her, and I wonder often if she regrets it. How she feels now that the trip from here back to Earth is farther than her time could span. No turning back, even if she wanted to. Some of the Terrans left behind family, or a family legacy. They have long histories, claim to be descended from the old explorer-colonizers, which always made me wonder if they joined the mission to carry on the family tradition. Mama tells me she never had any real anchors to the world when she left it. Nothing she could claim as part of her but me.

Was she looking for a legacy when she joined the ARK?

How did she feel, watching the world I've only ever seen in telescopes recede into a pale blue dot?

What does that much land feel like? To be in the open, breathing real air, not bounded by the walls of the ship?

***

I am the first human born in space.

They named me Virginia Dare. Which is, frankly, child cruelty disguised as historical mandate. (Virginia doesn't even exist anymore. It went under water after all the icebergs melted in 2034.) I prefer just being called Dare.

It could be worse: the second human born in space is named Tree. She says her parents must have been homesick.

Tree isn't alone. It's like confronting the scale of the cosmos for the first time incited an epidemic of uninspired baby names. Our parents named us after things we'd never get to see. That's probably some kind of metaphor for this whole ship. We're named for the places they remember, pieces of the real world in a place that was never meant to be forever.

Without even asking, we were created for the sole purpose of furthering a voyage we would never see the end of. The middle generation. I used to wonder how our parents could bring themselves to do that to us. But the only real difference between here and Earth is that we're in a smaller space. We were mostly a means to an end, and I guess I understand. Sacrifice the present for the future.

***

As we ready for bed in the adolescent dorm, the girl from the bunk below me tangles her fingers in mine. Her name is Verity, and unlike some of the more heavy-handed Earth-inspired names (mine included), Verity says her name means "truth" in Latin — a reminder of the ideals the mission serves, rather than what it left behind. When we were younger, Verity used to have a different name (it also meant "truth," but in a less interesting language); then she found a name that suited her more, walked right up to her parents, and changed it on the spot. I like this one a lot better. I have never understood why the Terrans insist on the cultural retention of Latin, a dead, annoying language, but the sound of her name makes me feel grateful that they do.

Space was never meant for humans, but I think I could live in the color of her eyes, dark as the place between stars. In the slumbering barracks, we whisper to each other. Her hand still has mine, and she squeezes it for emphasis. Our conversation is practiced for how often we've held it. It resembles a script.

Verity: "I wish we could leave. Steal a shuttle and go someplace new."

My rebuttal: "To where? Earth — the whole Sol System — is already too far behind us. There's nowhere to go, unless you think Pluto has magically become habitable."

"We could disappear. We would be like ghosts. Nobody just disappears here! They would make theories about us for centuries."

"The only place we could disappear to is into the vacuum of space. I'd prefer my respiratory system to continue functioning for the foreseeable future."

To which I am met with silence. Something for us both to reflect on — or maybe she just fell asleep.

The ship is never truly silent, of course. It rumbles and purrs, like a living thing. It would be quiet, Out there, for the thirty seconds I would live to know it.

It's not like I haven't considered it. A real "screw you" to the plan, and all, but that just means you're lost in the cosmos, drifting forever. Alone.

Here, slow though it is, at least we're moving. I want whatever components of me that are left to reach real ground one day.

Someday I'll die, and I will become one with the body of this place. Something has to fertilize the conservatory, after all. Waste is not an option in a closed system.

But if the ARK lives, even now, we're all in the cells of it, breaking new grounds for potential Theseus' ship parallels.

***

Verity loves the conservatory. I don't see the appeal. It's something we never got to have, and an imitation is hardly interesting to me. I still go with her to visit; the way she sets her cool hand on mine as she points, with heartfelt joy, at the fluttering bugs in the humid air, is motive enough. The butterflies were packed on the ship in huge numbers when our parents boarded, frozen eggs and a large living base to while away the generations with us. Not that they know any different — the only true Terran butterflies only lasted a few weeks, at most, into the voyage. Every time we go, Verity welcomes a new generation of those faceless, beautiful creatures, fledged with wing patterns Earth has never known. A microcosm of our own situation, from the bird's eye view.

I suppose that must be how the stars must feel, seeing us in frames of cosmic instants, from unimaginable distance. Everything is metaphoric from far enough away.

***

The thing I'm most grateful for about being trapped in a small metal box with the same people for the rest of my life is definitely that they're (mostly) not bigots. I am, honestly, relieved the ARK isn't some controlling authoritarian body that forces us to be straight and cis. Not that the experience is exclusive to people on a generation ship.

I don't live under a rock, just in one. I know there is a meaning to that twist in my stomach when I look at her lips. That there's a word for the way I ache when we're close. I know that I won't ever live the life my mom pictured for me when she got on this ship.

It's a little funny, actually? I mean, you get on a generation ship to get your descendants to some exoplanet, and your plan is foiled less than a century in because, of all things, your kid turns out to prefer women.

That's probably a little harsh on my mom — she's a very supportive parent. I think more than just genetic contribution, what matters to her is the community that we've built here. To be a part of something. The community will survive, I know it, so in a way, we will too. That's all she really wants, if she wants anything at all. I think maybe she just wanted to belong to something. Better space than a cult, I guess.

But the question is, what do *I* want?

I want it to be like this — this person I am, this thing curling in my ribs, these stars, this cosmic dark — forever. I want it to never be like this again. I am a twisting storm on the inside, and I have never felt the wind. I will only ever matter as an incremental part of something bigger than I will ever be, but that was always true. I want to feel a real sunbeam, just once.

But I never will, no matter how hard I wish.

I suppose the conservatory will have to do. The good news is, I have the perfect person to visit it with.

***

Life on a spaceship is not what I would have chosen for myself, I don't think. It's a restrictive world, and a finite one. To exist on it is to constantly confront the reality that someday, you won't, and the ship will carry on.

For all that, it has its perks. The endless void is a great date spot.

And as the ship we will die on shoots through the empty black, Verity and I attach the tethers to our borrowed spacesuits and we float, hand in hand.

It's not as quiet as I thought it would be, but the world obligingly narrows to just us all the same.

The stars align perfectly in this exact space and time, a pattern that only we will ever witness.

And I swear, I could chart a thousand constellations all of our own.

Monster/Love Is

by Alora Young

Monster

I like to think of my life as a silent movie
the motion is lost the moment
you close your eyes
or open the curtain
The urchins in the bottom of every
Body
Crawl out the throat in stop motion for any hope of being seen
Your secrets grow spines to tear through the movie screen
I'm choking on all the poetry I can never share with my family
It's my comfort in the closet and I use it to cover me my
First kiss will always be a biblical fallacy
I feel like Frankenstein
The villagers are hunting me the strength of my loves an affront to their bigotry and yet they still keep on calling me the monster
If I'm a beast of the night I can't help but wonder, what does that make them?
When they are loved by the people they try to condemn.
Frankenstein's monster had the mind of a child
hope in his heart a soul to be defiled by the hate they make a staple at every dinner table it's no wonder that
We all end up touch starved
The mark of the beast they hand carved
On to something pure
Because the different is not something
All righteous men can endure
I'd rather be what you call a monster
Than strip the smiles spread by "sin" and sonder
The hopeless heart's start to wish and wonder
If what it means to be a Bible child is worth the honor
lost a daughter

Gained an impostor
Haunted through the winter by the child you slaughter
When you say
No one would love that monster anyway

Love Is
When I was younger
I ripped love stories out of my fantasy books
I would hunger for pages with different outlooks
I prayed for paper
That didn't pierce my eyes
With its hopeless heteronormativity
I saw each stolen kiss as a vice
I made peace with a loveless life
but now these vices feel like virtues
I learned that love shouldn't hurt you
I understand
that I was looking for love in the wrong places
In the wrong hearts
I never found perfect symmetry
Because I searched for soulmates in parts
Now my stolen kisses
slip through pruned fingertips
My sublime wishes
Melt like acid drips
because society only cares
about the pieces that show in the shower
Bright eyes bring bitter skies
when you tell a butterfly not to love a flower
We swarm like bees to honey
soul to soul yin to yang
but they don't listen when our spirits screech

or when our bodies hang
But as sure as the cocoon
the butterfly does break free
So I'm gonna tell you what love is to me
Love is a library
it seems old and lonely and blue
but there's always a little corner
that belongs just to you.
Love isn't a lie
or a noble truth
It's not just a scam shrouded in youth
Love is a right
When it's denied
It's a prison
Love is always there
Even when they won't listen.
Love is holding someone as they slowly break down
Always knowing that one day
they'll hit the ground
Love is knowing the dark
comes back after the buzz
Love is praying they don't kill themselves
before the Molly does
Love is alone in a room full of people
because your heart is a million miles away
Love is only one-way glass
because their heart never decides to stay
Love is blood watered flowers
and cold tiled showers
and two mugs
two plates
two of everything,

to share
Love is someone
That, even when they're gone,
will always be there
No matter the form that love may take
no matter the heart that love may break
love,
is Love
is Love.

F— That

by Dylan P. Monahan

Content warning: anti-gay slur

My queerness does not refine me
My queerness does not define me
My ability to like a guy and get shy when he walks by only to want to ask him out feels impossible when walking down the street
The guy who's shredded and looks a thousand times better than me on the outside
Who's to say on the inside he's as broken as me only with a six pack

My queerness does not define me
I stare at guys hoping one day I might look like him
Walking down the underwear aisle at Kohl's when I'm eleven to find out
Fuck, what's wrong with me
Why can't I look like this?
Why won't I look like this?
I fear I'm stuck on an escalator that never moves
To see the world rise and fall with no one besides me looking at the time tick by

My queerness does not refine me
I go to the gym six days a week
Push pull leg push pull leg rest day
Push pull leg push pull leg rest day
Over and over and over again
Still seeing no change in that mirror while the time ticks by and my enemies and my competitors seem to blossom into who they want to become
Why aren't I looking like this?
What the fuck am I doing wrong?

My queerness does not define me
The thick walls I've built to block my soul from touching another is slowly starting to crumble as I see it was only a mask
One that would have broken by the sneeze of a dog
Maybe one day I can be as strong as that dog
To stand tall in hopes that someone notices the impact I have on my surroundings but at last I'm looking into that mirror seeing no change
The ideology of the gym and physique is one I never expected to find only to realize after fourteen months that my appearance and my mindset was altered by the stereotypes that lead us queer babies
The models of our world have led me like many other queers down a path of self-destruction while prohibiting our process to grow and alter our goals to what we want rather than what they have
Why is it that the models, the straights, the influencers and the bullies rule my life when I'm in the front seat driving down the highway hoping to reach my destination that seems a billion miles away
Except it's not my destination, but the journey my society has told me to take to find the right match when I'm shredded like the guy walking down the street that I blushed at but couldn't say a word

My queerness has defined me
My queerness has built into an alter-persona I take on every time I step foot out of my room leaving what's really me hidden in the shadows of my appearance
My queerness has given me the anxiety when I see that guy and the notion that I'm not enough
Who the fuck gets to say I'm not enough?
That I'm not enough for myself?
That I'm not enough for love?
Who the fuck gave me the concept that I'm fucked up in every way possible?
That my life was not ok even though gay is "okay"

My queerness has given me the wall I have and made me shut my doors to love
In that I am having to reevaluate every God damn decision in my life for that it might not be enough for anyone
For me

I've come to far out of the closet to realize I will never be able to shut it closed
That the room I would be entering into would be filled with mindless bullshit to shove me back in and say, "You belong here"
I belong in the closet because that's the only thing I know
I belong in the closet because according to society standards, I'm still a fag
I belong in the closet because some right-wing conservative tells me to go kill myself because I like kissing men
Society has taught me that I'm not enough compared to that shredded man walking down the street because I'm a fag who can't walk on his own god damn two feet
Fuck that

Drama Class

by Caleb Adams

Do you remember when we were in Drama?

1st period. Freshman year.

We were searching — no scouring — for monologues to which we could relate

I found five for you.

For me we found none.

I found it silly how those books were divided.

Male

Female

Male

Female

Do you remember the week before?

The teacher in front of the class, lecturing us on choosing one that fit with "who we are"

who I am. What a laughable concept

Who am I?

"If you're a girl, do a monologue as a girl"

If only it was as simple as that.

It's a choice between acceptance of others or acceptance of myself.

As a child, I was taught never be selfish

"Good girls don't behave that way"

I wish I could be that 'good girl' you want me to be

I'm no good girl

I am tears and skin and fears and sin

Nothing I do I do for me

Pandemonium

by Aubrey Roche

Rain thundered down in cascading sheets, and the uproar echoed throughout the car. The radio played on, and though I could hardly hear it over the noise, I recognized it as a U2 song I always liked but could never remember the name of for some reason. Eva in the passenger seat hummed along, and there was quiet between us. It seemed almost peaceful, driving through the rain with nothing surrounding us, save for thick pine forests and open road.

Our Saturday afternoon was passing quickly, and we were expected to be home before dark. It was hard to tell when it would be dark, though; dreary, gray clouds had floated in earlier and the sun was nowhere to be found. Because it was raining so hard, I wanted to get home sooner rather than later. All I could do was drive. Which was difficult, too, even with the windshield wipers going as fast as they could go. I drove just under the speed limit, even though we were alone on the road.

"Pull over," Eva said suddenly. I glanced over at her, nervous to even take my eyes off the road for a second, and a large, ecstatic grin filled her face.

"Why?" I asked. I couldn't imagine what she needed, and nothing appeared to be wrong with her, judging by her expression.

"I want to dance in the rain. I want to feel it." She sounded ethereal and as though she'd never experienced pouring rain before.

"We're driving in the middle of a storm, and you want to stop and feel the rain?" I replied in disbelief. "You've got to be kidding me. You'll get soaking wet! And then you'll have to sit and be miserable for the rest of the drive."

"I don't care about getting wet. I just want to do something crazy like this before I have to go home and do nothing but study. Just pull over. Please, Madelyn."

I knew that if I didn't, she would continue to pester me and even start to claim that I wasn't capable of having any fun. Nobody was coming and no one was behind us, so I pulled into the shoulder of the road. Eva burst out of her door, but I first rummaged around in the backseat for my jacket, then zipped it up all the way and flipped my hood on, which still didn't stop me from getting soaked. Eva had abandoned her coat. After I got out, I stayed on the shoulder, to keep safe on the off chance that somebody did come racing through.

Eva's T-shirt hung around her, already soaked, and her hair hung in twisted, tangled tendrils. She had to have been freezing cold, but she didn't seem to mind at all. She spun in a circle with her arms spread wide open, a tremendous smile filling up half of her face and her eyes closed. She opened them and instantly saw me standing and shivering, my whole body shaking and my arms crossed over my chest.

I stood for a moment in awe, just watching her and watching how free and happy she seemed, out of the harsh grip of her parent's rules and the weight of advanced classes. I wished she could be like this all the time, carefree and doing silly things that didn't matter. I rarely got to see this side of Eva.

Once I felt water soaking through to my toes, I realized that standing out in the rain for much longer wasn't a very good idea. I shouldn't have gotten out of the car in the first place, and if I hadn't, I would still be warm and dry right now. I should've just waited for her to do this. Who was I kidding, though? I knew I'd follow Eva anywhere.

She stopped dancing and bounded over towards me. I stood there with my arms crossed, trying to retain whatever warmth I could, and her eyes met mine. They were open wide, round and brown and beautiful. Before I could say anything, she kissed me. It felt like we were in a movie, except I could hardly stop shivering for long enough to kiss her back. Her mouth felt cool, and my damp hand trembled as I brushed it along her cheek. When she pulled away, she was smiling again, and she returned to the road. She still hadn't said a single word.

Eva stood with her chin pointed towards the sky and her arms stretched out, as though spreading her wings. She had her back to the oncoming traffic, and that's when I realized that there was oncoming traffic — and Eva was standing directly in the center of the road.

"Eva, move!" I screamed.

She threw herself towards me, just barely managing to land out of the path of travel of a shiny red sedan. She had landed on the ground, and I pulled her up, asking if she'd gotten hurt. She shook her head, and I pulled her into a bone-crushing hug. She clung to me desperately, her arms curling around my back and her face buried in my shoulder. In that moment when I saw the car coming, every emotion seemed to flood through me. I thought for a split second that I might lose her, and I didn't want to fathom anything beyond that.

But that didn't happen, and I'd never before felt such a strong sense of relief.

"You sure you're okay?" I asked again. She nodded slowly, and I helped her back to the car. We were both drenched, but there wasn't much we could do about it. Any time it would take to find a towel or blanket in the trunk would've just made everything even wetter.

When I got in the driver's side door, I didn't start the car back up right away. "God, Eva, you scared me." My hands and voice were both shaking, and I sat on my hands to try and warm them up.

I could hear her teeth chattering as she said quietly, "I know."

"I don't want anything to happen to you," I continued, but then I paused. "I love you."

Before, I hadn't been sure, but in that frantic moment, I knew. I loved her. I loved her so much. And we'd never said it before, even after we confessed our feelings for each other months ago. Now, I'd never felt anything stronger.

She turned to look at me, her sopping-wet hair curling around her face, reminding me of her beautiful eyes right before she kissed me. "Really?"

"Yeah."

"I love you too."

"See?" My voice grew higher, cracking almost as I fought back tears. "I thought I might lose you. And it was the worst second of my life."

"I'm sorry," she answered, looking down at her jeans, which were dark with water. I could only imagine how uncomfortable they were, clammy and stuck against her legs.

Then I did start the car, turning on the heat, but keeping it in park. "You don't have to be sorry. But I just ... I wanted you to know how I feel. Because I was scared you were going to die before I could tell you."

"It was stupid. Honestly." She answered.

"Yeah. But it's okay." I shifted the car into drive and turned off the parking brake. "Let's go home."

She nodded, pulling her jacket tighter around her. The heat was at full blast, but neither of us were beginning to dry. We still had about half an hour of driving to do, and I began to imagine what I would tell my dad as to why I was all wet. As I drove, I took a quick glance at Eva next to me. She was sitting on her hands, probably desperate for warmth, but still shaking and still soaked. I didn't know what else I could do to help. There wasn't much we could do until we got home.

I had turned the radio off, but the U2 song we were listening to played through my head once again. It was a beautiful day.

The Girl with Green and Yellow Eyes

by B. Carfagno

I've never quite liked the color yellow
I was too sunny, too vibrant
I seemed to hurt my eyes
But that changed when I'd see her

I didn't understand at first,
But I'd see her eyes
with their yellow-green swirl,
and the color seemed to take on a whole new meaning.

Yellow became my favorite color
My mother questioned it, but still agreed to entertain my new color obsession

She still believed I would marry the boy next door
How could I tell her otherwise?

Her little girl, with cropped hair, and tired eyes is a stranger
Clad in yellow
Staring not at the boy next door, but his sister
Staring at the girl with green and yellow eyes.

Nihilism for My High School Sweetheart

by E.T. McGinley

so yes, pretty girl.
one of these days we will probably break up.
we will get older, and grow apart,
and this relationship will not be a trellis
but harvest left so long on the vine
it rotted. the bough of your arm will weigh heavy
on my shoulders — my hand will not entwine
quite so sweetly with yours.

We know these things in the same way
that we know we will soon move away
from our family dogs, or that the sun
is going to implode; too much
to trifle ourselves with now. We shall
worry instead about the tangible:

holding hands in public (should we
shouldn't we, and if we do,
what happens when our palms get sweaty
or men on street corners stare too long?)

first kisses (ours was in your car
and my driveway, between the stone wall
succumbing to Boston ivy and the rotted oak
that's got to come down
one of these days)

my Facebook status (updated,
of course, within minutes;
I have no patience for locking

ourselves in privacy, for fear
it feels all too much like a closet)

but today, I suppose,
we are young and happy. I, for one,
am willing to let us grow
in the comfortable shadow
of forever.

Forced Perfection

by Shahelle

I was born gay, Hispanic, daughter of immigrants, and a woman. I'm the embodiment of diversity points. To make life harder, I was born Mormon. I learned to live and adapt to the white, conservative, Christian world. I learned to say the right things and look the right way. I could recite rules and passages, dress perfectly and always smile to show my light and for a long time. It was genuine. I loved it — I loved the praise, the attention, and the support.

But the second I stopped smiling, the applause silenced, the support was nowhere to be seen, and my life changed. One act, one man changed everyone's perception of me. Who knew a white man could have so much power. I was a victim and a child, he was a grown man and a criminal, but somehow, he got everyone on his side. I was told to forgive and forget, and the same verses I used to recite were thrown in my face and used to silence my voice. My words fell on deaf ears when I screamed that I was still the same, they saw me as rebellious because I didn't talk anymore, I didn't smile, I wasn't happy. Being unhappy was equated to falling away, to being unrighteous. But I couldn't be happy, forced to see the man who ruined everything every Sunday. I couldn't be happy when they told me I should've stayed away, when I was forced to relive the story every time my mind drifted. Once my world changed, I grasped at the remains until they completely faded away.

Once they faded away, I let myself finally breathe. I no longer acted, dressed, or smiled for praise. As I discovered myself, my first crush came, and she was gorgeous. I refused to let myself believe that it wasn't more than straight admiration for her looks and personality, the way she laughed and dressed — but it *was* more. Months went by and the warm feeling never left. I felt something that I had never felt for a guy, something my friends so vividly described when talking about their schoolboy crushes. I would panic and name the first guy that popped into my mind, obsess over him and say a stupid thing about his eyes. I refused to forget the lie I'd been told that my love was a sin and I was meant to be happy with some cute Mormon boy, one who could recite verses with me and create a family. There is nothing wrong with this fantasy, if it's what you feel you want, but for me, it was fear of being cast away and seen as nothing unless I upheld this standard of a perfect life.

I came out pretty quickly as bi but was still stuck on the idea of the sin of "same-sex attraction." I was sure I was going to one day meet the right man and live the straight life, but I kept meeting men and they were all not my type. I cried and prayed a lot to be changed, to be normal, to feel what my friends felt for guys, but I stayed the same. For years it seemed that no matter what I did, I couldn't find happiness. I blamed myself, I blamed that man who lives his life normally while I'll never forget that one night.

But then I let go of the lie of myself being a sin. I painfully let go of the idea of that perfect family, and stopped seeing it as same-sex attraction, but as who I love, who I am and who I'm happy with. People will often say why parade it around, why force it down our throats, if you're happy you shouldn't have to prove it, but I'm not trying to prove it — I'm just fighting for my equal rights, showing you can be happy without the stereotypical love story.

When people stop screaming misquoted Bible verses in my face, when I don't get told to repent for my sins, when church no longer feels like a hate group, I might stop parading my sexuality around. When straight isn't the norm and queer isn't feared, when people aren't kicked out of their homes for being themselves, then we'll stop "pushing our sexualities down your throat." But we're fighting to be seen as equal, to not be called sinners, for people to understand that it isn't just who you sleep with but it's who you love, it's how you feel, it's more than worldly desires that can be pushed away — if you push them away, you're denying yourself.

You can't pray to be changed and be "normal." If it was possible, don't you think thousands of children wouldn't be gone from this earth, gone because they tried desperately to change who they were? I didn't choose to feel this way, I didn't give in to anything because if I could, I would have been straight. I tried to be straight. Don't you think it would be a lot easier to conform to what you've been taught your whole life than go against everything you know? No one chooses who they are, how they feel. Our love is no more sinful or different than love that is straight.

Dance

by Maximillian Romanov

Dance. Dance and sweat.

Sway your hips to the left. Now the right.

Brush that hair out of your face.

Don't check the time. You know it's late. Or early technically. Either way it's past midnight.

Steer clear of that dude. He seems coked out.

More swaying.

Make eye contact. Now drop your eyes. Play coy.

Drop down into a squat. Stand upright and shake your hips a bit more.

Check to see if he's still watching.

He is.

Take off your shirt. It's cheap so don't feel bad about tossing it aside.

Damn hair. You should get it cut. For now just brush it away again.

The music is pounding but that's okay. Block it out.

Is he watching?

Yes?

Good.

Make eye contact and keep it.

Make sure he knows you see him.

In this sea of bodies, a huddled mass of sweaty muscled bodies. This gathering of adonizes.

Turn around. Show off your butt. Your mating call.

Throw him a wink.

Keep swaying. Wait for him to come to you.

Should you go to the bar?

No. Better stay sober.

That asshole just slammed into you.

Screw it ignore him.

He's not worth the effort.

Look back. Is he still there?

Yes?

Good.

He seems to be trying to get closer. To fight through the swarm of guys.

Caught him.

Smile.

Go back to swaying. Faster. Shake your hips. Now slow down. Follow the rhythm.

Someone's tapping your shoulder. Turn around.

It's him.

"Hey there beautiful"

You can barely hear him.

Well say something. Something witty or cool.

"Hello to you too."

4/10. Try better next time.

"I'm Pe-"

Peter? Is that what he said?

Don't ask. You'll seem unattentive.

Do you think he's interested?

Put your hands on his hips.

Wow. He so warm.

He hasn't stopped you. He likes it. He's smiling.

Good.

"I'm Adrian."

Were you loud enough? Did he hear you?

"You're very cute Adrian."

Okay that was unmistakable. He's smiling. You like his smile. It isn't creepy or pervy like some guys.

"You too. Come here often?"

Good enough. 7/10.

"Only -n spe- occasion-"

Okay. That kinda made sense.

If only the music was quieter.

Get closer. Chest to chest.

His hands are on your hips. It's amazing.

Dance together. Hips together. Chests together.

Look up. He's a bit taller.

He's looking at you too.

Say something.

"I don't do this often."

Pray that he heard you.

A grin. He did.

"- fate"

Fate.

Yeah that sounds right.

Wow he's magnetic.

His hips are flush with your own.

If only he wasn't wearing that pesky shirt.

His hands move up. Your lower back.

Mirror his actions.

Slip your hands under his shirt.

He seems to like it.

Turn around again.

His hands on your stomach, yours on his thighs.

His jeans seem worn but like in a fashionable sense.

His hands move up again. Your chest, pulling you back closer to him.

He's so warm.

Ignore the butterflies.

Dance.

Sweat.

Try to reach around. Your hands on his hips.

You feel breath on your neck.

Did he just chuckle?

Oh if only you hadn't turned around.

He turns you around.

Well that's that problem solved.

Should you kiss him?

No not yet.

The club is way too loud. I guess that's to expect from a gay club.

They do love to flaunt don't they?

You would know.

His smile. It's dazzling.

More sweat, more gyrating.

Louder music.

Lose yourself.

Enjoy it.

The hands.

The noise.

The heat.

The intimacy.

The lack of privacy.

The bustling bodies.

The feeling of being the only two people there.

Okay,

Kiss him.

"Happy New Years!"

Everyone is cheering.

He's smiling.

"Happy 1988 Peter."

"It's Percy."

Well you fucked that up.

"Well you wanna take me home, Percy?"

"Let's dance a bit more."

To Be an American

by Justin Anthony Hartley

What does it mean to be an American? Is it where you grew up? Where you lived? Where you were born? Your nationality? Where your ideologies lie? Who do you follow? What do you do?

To be an American, what does it mean? Hell, what even is an "American" to begin with?

Are you really an American when your race is underscored? Are you really an American when your sexuality is questioned? Are you really an American when your road to freedom is hindered? What about when hyphens expound your differences? When your economic status is met with pauses? When your gender is seen as fallacy?

Are you American when you're exotified and corrected?

Corrected for your blackness? Corrected for your existence?

What do you do when your being is questioned? What do you do when your life is examined?

Interrogated?

Challenged?

Searched?

And prodded?

Who is America built for? Who is America for? Is America for whiteness and layers of privilege? Is America for those who exhibit its ideals?

You often find when you are born as a question, as a footnote in the history of other men, you inquire: Is America for me? Is America for you? Or is America for all of us? Or just for the some?

Tell me, tell me, tell me now! For I need to know. Is America for us? Is America for you? Is America for me?

For I fear I may begin to disappear.

Let me tell you, I am an American with all my gayness, my blackness, and all my other -isms and -nesses. I am an American.

I believe this country can do better.

I believe this country can do better.

That we should recognize and face the errors of our past, embrace them, place them front and center in our experiences. We must bellwether our society for progress because injustice does not correct itself when asked or clotted. Injustice perishes when people destroy it, defeat it.

Give it a name and scrawl upon the face of hate and inequity with your mightiest pen. Draw out the rainbows and skies of the future over the antagonists of days past. Root out the impurities, burn them from their cores and bury the leftovers. Let Columbia and Lady Liberty fulfill their promises to the masses, give home to those huddled masses looking for freedom. Embrace Americans in all of their forms, cloak them in your warmth, grasping hold their needing hands, give them their destinies. The ones the majority has been afforded. Unmask the obscurities, reach into the great other and pull out those shrouded in the benighted veneer of institutionalization out into the day.

Let America satisfy the whims of its creation, to satisfy those who are drawn into its melting pot. Look at our broken history and our dilapidated state, stare at it in all its repugnance and our abhorrent natures.

We stamp it out in whatever way possible. We must cast out injustice as if it were war or a creature going bump in the night.

I ask you. I beg you. Illuminate me. My name is Justin Hartley.

I have no other name. The rest are simply misnomers.

8/1/2019

by maysie jane

i'm no good at love poems
i wasn't built with rom coms
or too big candy hearts
sweet nothings meant nothing
and the kiss at the end of the movie was just a kiss
i never fell in love with people
i made connections with other things
i found a captivation in the stars
turned my head towards the sunflowers and serenaded sweet honey
i was content being infatuated with me
i was never scared of my own "i love yous"

i liked people in a paper sense
my very own affection for the beings that
make music and craft poems
spreading your mouth wide isn't a sign of danger

wolves don't like baring teeth
but for us
this is home

one that i often
stayed locked out of

then one day
i looked up

i met a pair of eyes
that the stars fell down for
a body sunflowers

wished they could grow on
and a head made of sweet honey
and full of sweet somethings
this was a person crafted with the things i taught myself to fall in love with
and there it went
girl meets girl
girl likes girl
and slowly
but surely i taught myself to fall in love with her too
with her
intimacy didn't seem like a trap
slow dancing with no music was no longer a cliche
it only took a day and then some
for me to run straight into her arms

romeo and juliet can't hold a flame to us
because living in a world where each kiss is revolutionary
we can't have a flame
we need a whole forest fire
and everything's better when it's gay anyway
right?

one day she called me soft
and now that word means so much more
no longer something used to describe the blanket she gave me
it means a multitude of personality and perfection
peachy lips
and walt whitman

i was never any good at love poems
but she was made to have love poems written about her

Trichotillomania

by Sofia Picornell

"Oh my god, why don't you have eyelashes?"

I quickly looked around to see if anyone else heard before responding, "I was in the car one day trying to curl them when we came to a quick stop and they all got pulled out."

"You were curling both eyes at once?"

"Yep, it sucks," I stammered.

I knew that was the most unbelievable story I could have come up with. It didn't even make sense. God this was so embarrassing.

As I got off the bus that day, I walked to my house, grabbed a quick snack, and settled in my room. I took out my math homework that I had no interest in doing and scanned the first few problems. I got bored within a minute of trying and instinctively felt my fingers go to my eyelids. Without any reluctance, I watched as the pile grew from a few to about a dozen on the edge of my paper. I brushed it off and continued with my work as if nothing happened.

I never thought it would get this bad. It became a pattern and even my friends' parents were telling me, "Something looks different about you." I liked to think that it was because I looked older; entering the sixth grade was a big deal and all. I just wish I didn't have to deal with this on top of everything.

For the past year I had become addicted to pulling out my eyelashes. I bet you're thinking, "Why would anyone ever want to do that?" or "Doesn't that hurt?" Those are the same questions my parents had when they repeatedly told me to stop and didn't understand why I wouldn't listen. Mirrors became my worst enemy as they constantly reminded me of my failure to control myself. I guess it became enough of a problem that my parents decided I needed outside help.

The summer before sixth grade, my parents took me to see a counselor who specialized in kids with habits like mine. The drive there could not have been more tedious. I was too embarrassed to even think about talking to someone about why I did it, because if I was being honest, I wasn't sure I knew the answer. Once I started, I just couldn't stop. I just needed to get every last eyelash out before I could focus on doing anything else.

As we pulled into the lot, both of my parents got out and led me inside. It was one of those boring offices with a long skinny hallway and identical doors set to the right and left side. The blandness of the hallway gave me a horrible first impression. I knew she was going to be some boring lady who wouldn't understand anything, because no one ever did. I was led into a small waiting room with a few toys, some seats, and plain white walls. It was hard for me not to start crying right then and there. I felt sick. I just wanted to go home, and I definitely didn't want to talk to a stranger.

She came out and introduced herself, then led us into her office. We took a seat on the couch and I immediately felt a tear start to roll down my cheek. Before the questions started, she took the time to introduce herself again and explain what she did and how she would help me. She explained that I had Trichotillomania, a hair-pulling mental disorder that involves recurrent, irresistible urges to pull out hair from any area of your body. For me, it was my eyelashes. I was told that this was very common in kids around my age of eleven and to not feel embarrassed because there were probably other kids at my school going through the same thing.

I left that session with some tricks for how to stop myself from pulling out eyelashes, or as we called it, "picking." That night we tried the first trick. When going to bed, I zip-tied a pair of gloves around my hands so that I couldn't get them off when I felt an urge coming on. I could not help but think about how weird this would look to an outside eye, wrapping up my hands like they were some sort of weapon. I made it clear to my parents that I was too ashamed to wear anything preventive to school or while I was hanging out with friends.

***

It is the morning of my eighth grade graduation. I put on my dress and move on to the bathroom. As I look in the mirror, I can't help but smile back at myself, proud of everything I have accomplished these past few years. My mother allowed me to put on some makeup for the occasion. I think back to last year when I first started showing signs of improvement. Even my parents say I seem to stand taller nowadays. I gained a sense of self-respect and no longer think of myself as powerless against my condition. Tearing myself away from my image, I make my way downstairs, my thoughts focused on my future ahead.

Closets Aren't for Kids

by Max Sanborn

The moment someone is able to discern you,
The real you,
Is possibly the most terrifying,
And liberating,
Feeling one can experience

The feeble shaking of your once impenetrable facade,
The same one that had been so laborious to build,
Curtly coming to its imminent end
At the hands of an amiable smile
And meticulous fingers
Is like a full night's sleep
To a struggling insomniac,
Like a teeming cup of coffee
To first time parents
Kept up all night by the guttural screams of a newborn

But the road has only begun,
And damn, if it isn't one of the hardest things you'll do

It is a precipitous road,
One that will lead you through rivers
That sluice about, soaking your shoes

It will steer you right over chasms
That make your voice echo back with an unfamiliar ire
Lacing every lie the old you once told with a pungent feel
That leaves an acrid taste lingering in your mouth

It will force you to recreate yourself

Or to succumb to the ones that lurk in your periphery
You either move forward
Or you become one of them

Their unkempt look,
Their faces, plagued by permanent grimaces,
Sallow and taut, as if life itself has made them ill
They beg you to stay with them
"You're safe here"
"You don't know what they do to people like us"

No, never
You continue on
Because what other choice do you have?
So you feign energy and life
Because you can finally see the end of the road
The end of everything fake,
The moment of salvation,
Of freedom after years of interminable captivity

Your face sheens with sweat as the road comes to an end
And you are once again met by the merciful eyes of the one who started it all,
Who pulled you out of the darkness
And showed you a world where being you wasn't so bad after all

You hope that one day the ones with the gaunt faces and tortured eyes
Will join you in this new, beautiful world
After all, closets aren't for kids anymore

It's Not Over Yet

by Natalie Kelly

"Don't take it personally," I explained to my little sister as I opened the White-Out, letting the clinical alcohol smell diffuse across the room. "They don't mean it like that."

She didn't respond, too captivated with the office supplies she was not supposed to touch. I carefully brushed over the word "father" each time it appeared on the page. Within a few seconds the solution had dried, allowing me to replace the inadequate word with the more accurate word: "mother."

According to our mothers, our belligerence was futile — the school did not care what type of parents we had, as long as they knew who to contact when an emergency happened. My ten-year-old sister, however, was not convinced and insisted on fixing their mistake. At twelve, I had realized it was not usually a mistake, but rather a misunderstanding. When you have two mothers, you're used to this kind of misunderstanding from anyone coming from a nuclear family.

It's easy to not notice the little things. At age five, I could ignore the lady asking my mother if my dad was Chinese or Japanese. While she condoned mixed families, the woman could not yet accept unorthodox ones. At seven, I was unbothered by TV characters who always had mommies and daddies. I delighted in a book with families that resembled mine, *ABC: A Family Alphabet Book*, but I soon grew out of learning the alphabet. Still, I never wondered why *Harry Potter* contained only "normal" families.

In second grade, I switched from a Quaker private school to Unionville Elementary, a public school where I was one of only five Asians, another factor that set me apart. When I was asked to introduce myself, I announced that I had "two mommies" as a fun fact. I didn't know any better. The next day, a boy in my class called me gay. Only eight years old, I didn't know what that word meant, but I knew it wasn't a compliment. The teasing was incessant until he moved away in middle school. Of course, not all of my new classmates acted like he had — most didn't care.

Years later, when my best friend asked why I had two moms, I explained that I was adopted, hoping she would assume there were two "normal" families behind me: one that gave me up and one that took me in. Revealing as little information as possible about myself seemed to be the only way to avoid weird looks and name-calling, even from those I trusted. Although I was proud of my family, I was shy and willing to hide behind a fabrication of the truth to keep friends.

My worst fears were confirmed when a new friend in middle school had strong religious beliefs against my family. Using the "love the sinner, hate the sin" rhetoric I had learned to despise, she attempted to pray the gay away at a birthday party. I went home, cried, and vowed to never go to her house again.

Interpersonal relationships were not the only difficulty. Everywhere I went, it seemed like the world just could not wrap its head around the idea of two moms. I spent years of my life correcting misconceptions. During family dinners out, waiters would automatically print out separate checks in whatever way they decided to fracture my family. Instead of changing forms, I wrote my mother's feminine name next to "Dad" and hoped the school would understand that I didn't, in fact, have a father. Sitting in a doctor's office, I explained that I had an alternative family and wouldn't know any medical history. My parents, I knew, had faced larger discrimination and couldn't be bothered with the little things. They were happy to be able to adopt children, to work, and to be accepted by their families. My sister and I focused on the annoyances in life, in part due to teen angst and in part because we had never known worse.

In 2015, gay marriage was legalized and celebration occurred across the country. My parents' best friends got married that summer. My moms chose not to for a multitude of reasons, including the complexity of changing foreign adoption papers, further cementing in others' minds that even among weird families, we were weirder.

When asked about homophobia, most people will say it no longer exists, that it's 2017, and that society's standards have become more accepting than ever. Some of these statements are becoming increasingly valid as being LGBTQ+ becomes more mainstream. Most of my classmates are mature enough to understand that differences and diversity are the cornerstones of American society. Some, however, answer a school survey and put "transvestite" as their gender, or use "gay" as an insult on the bus.

There will always be people who either can't understand my family or simply choose not to. Unfortunately, there will also always be people who believe we have come so far that we can stop now. But we cannot forget that even after the government ended slavery, people of color had to march in the streets to have equal societal treatment; even after women were given the right to vote, they had to fight to be recognize in the workplace and independent of men. We have to work harder not only for equal treatment, but to prove to society that it's not there yet.

The Warmth of Women

by Anaya Patel

He pulls you in close,
Your head rests in his chest,
His bare skin barely showing beneath his blue v-neck,
You can smell the cheap cologne he bought from Macy's.

He looks down at you,
Your eyes meet,
His bright blue, dazzling from the veil of credulity,
Soft, with more to say than you want to hear.

He pulls your chin to his,
His hands caressing your cheek,
His lips kissing you softly,
With passion and ego and love.

He pulls away,
His eyes finding yours once more,
He grins,
His lips parting to a smile that curves and shows his dimples.

But you look past him.
And you see her,
Wearing a bright red sundress with white flowers and Docs to match,
Her dark skin glistening in the sun rays.

Your eyes meet,
And you see the face of God.

The world freezes.
The clouds slow, stop, and rewind,

Even time, the most merciless of them all, faces defeat.

The skies and the trees and the strangers fade until it's just
You, her, and horizon.

But you freeze with it.
Locked in place,
Stuck in a moment with a hole the size of your heart.

Separated by past and present and distance and love and hatred and ache,
A tear rolls down your cheek,
And somehow,
She can feel it on her bright red sundress.

Your heart grows heavy,
Your mind becomes foggy,
Your limbs lose feeling,
And you force yourself to look back at him.

You stare vacantly into his bright blue eyes, scanning and reading
And trying to listen and hearing only white noise.
You feel out of place, out of body, out of touch with reality.
More tears run down your cheek, your face a canvas for black ink,
But he can't see the harrowing art you display.
Only she can.

You can feel her piercing gaze,
But you refuse to look up.

You stare at him while he holds you and kisses you and tells you he loves you,
And as you cry with the force of a million longing souls, you tell him you love him back.

Reach for Me

by Danny

2019 Scholarship Runner Up

August 8th, 2000, a baby girl is born
she is carved from the womb of her mother covered in flower petals the doctors paint pink
her lungs are fragile
her ears, they say, not meant to hear the sweet nothings that spill from coddling parents
her eyes not meant to see the beauty of the world around her, but instead designed to shatter into nothing but
fragmented glass
And she
she is delicate and soft
kissed by a dozen tulips
she is brought to life
to live
a miracle, some may say
And still
she grows
but not under the care of her mother
who is chained by an act of her childhood
Instead she is held under the blackened thumb of her father
a man whose heart beats to a tune only he cares to listen to
and she remains quiet and still
an enclosed shell of who she could be wrapped tightly around herself
And she never questions why she doesn't like pink or dresses
she grows
and with growth, there is change
change she doesn't like as red runs in rivulets from her and suddenly
suddenly everything is different
She is different

and she never questions why
or even how
since the one time she did she was scolded for her ignorance
For how could a girl become a boy?
but why is a simple part of flesh
capable of placing who she is
she prefers jeans and art
fantasy and superheroes
paintings and dogs
And yet
when given an answer to her question
she stops
she accepts the pink flowers growing all around her rather than plucking at them
she still doesn't like make-up or dresses
that scream a version of womanhood
often times she feels as though she were a puzzle piece designed for a different puzzle
It hits her when she's sixteen sitting in a car
glancing at pictures and she realizes
with no warning
rearranging the molecules that designed her
that she
She is not a she
But a he
He is different
still he tries to push the revelation away
tries to reason with himself
but it wasn't a phase
he acts as if these feelings
this vision of himself
skin crawling

unable to hear his own name as anything but a curse
muttered by others like a sin
he acts like everything ought to be discarded
as if being a man is like being the moon
that he's taken someone else's light
and being a man will only last a little while
but he was wrong
he can no longer lie to himself
to others
he spent so long as she hiding behind a shell of shyness and hushed words
never speaking of how Dad behaves
but his dad is gone
And he was too focused on living long enough to grow older
never able to look at the sky to see a constellation that was his alone
but now he has and he wants and wants and wants
to live as
Him
The world only sees pink petals dotting his chest
as though the flowers couldn't change
It hurts
vines curl and twist around him
as if every bit of rejection doesn't bat an eye at how he can't breathe
because being stuck in his body is the worst agony
he wants to rip himself open as though he were a mere patient on an operating table
Maybe one day he will be
One day the flowers on his chest will be removed
and he can wear his scars proudly
knowing he's happier
He will mourn his family
and those lost along the way
But he will grow and change

He doesn't choose this; he chooses happiness

August 8th, 2018

He is still he

and he

is changing.

A Friend Among Foes

by Al Stoots

Content warning: bullying

The alarm clock rang annoyingly as Erin woke up from sleep. She turned off the alarm on her phone and got up. Today was her first day of high school: freshman year. She was terrified for what was to come. What if people didn't like her? What if they bullied her? What if she ended up alone? All these "what-ifs" crossed her mind, but she couldn't focus on that now — she had to get ready for the day.

She planned her outfit the night before and chose a cute sleeveless button up and a skirt. Erin got dressed and went to the bathroom to brush her hair. She then put on some light makeup. She wasn't used to it but was glad her older sister Lyla taught her how to apply it properly. The first time around was a complete disaster, and Erin's sister had walked in on her. Lyla was determined to make her sister look good. *She's the best*, Erin thought.

She went back to her room, grabbed her backpack, and headed downstairs. That's when she saw that her dad was home. She was hoping he would have left by now. He looked at her and was disappointed. Just seeing him like that made Erin restless.

Her dad spoke, "I thought we discussed this. You look like a mess, E—"

"Erin and I have to leave now, dad!" Erin's sister interrupted, walking down the stairs.

Lyla picked up a couple of snacks for breakfast and grabbed her car keys. Erin's dad looked fairly annoyed. Erin felt her sister grab her arm and quickly pull her out of the house. Lyla was indeed in a rush to get out but still stayed her chipper self.

"Okay dad, love you, bye!" Lyla quickly spoke as she closed the door.

Her dad sighed once more, "What am I going to do about those two…"

Erin and Lyla hopped into the car and drove off. Erin didn't realize it before, but she felt the tension in her body relax. Her jaw hurt as she realized her teeth were clenched. She turned on the radio to her favorite music station, which typically consisted of the latest hits. Lyla looked over to her younger sister. Erin swore she saw a bit of concern on Lyla's face, but it quickly went away.

"So, are you excited for high school?" Lyla asked.

"Uh … no, not really," Erin replied.

She had no need to lie to her sister. Lyla had always been there for her, even if Erin felt she was a bit annoying.

Lyla laughed, "Yeah, I felt the same way on my first day. Now look at me! Three years later and I am a senior ready to get this year started."

"No one enjoys going to school, Lyla," Erin remarked.

Lyla gave up the act, "Yeah you're right I hate it."

They both laughed. After turning the corner, they could see the school building, and Erin felt her nervousness return.

Lyla parked in the parking lot. She looked like she wanted to say something but didn't know how to say it. She finally spoke, "Look, Erin, if … anyone gives you a hard time today, please let me know. I might not be able to help in the moment, but I'm always ready to support my little sister."

Erin felt herself tearing up a bit from happiness, "Thank you. I'll keep that in mind … But I'm sure you would just beat them up."

Lyla elbowed Erin, "Darn right I would! No one messes with my family!"

Erin chuckled. They got out of the car and headed to the front of the building. On the way there, Erin observed the people going by. No one in particular looked extremely friendly, but no one looked like they were going to beat her up. *I guess it's a good thing?* Erin thought to herself.

The two sisters entered the building. If the outside wasn't confusing enough, the inside was definitely puzzling. Erin pulled out her schedule from her backpack.

Lyla looked at it and wrote where Erin would find her classes. "Don't get lost, and don't be late! Actually, if you get lost, you can ask an upperclassman. Trust me they are not here to hurt you. They remember what being a freshman was like. I'll see you later!"

Lyla headed off to her class. Erin watched as her sister left. She took a deep breath and headed to her first block.

It was a bit hard to get there, but Erin managed quite well on her own. As she passed by other students in the hall, she became worried. She feared they were all judging her as she walked by.

She walked into class. Thankfully, it was fairly empty since it would take a while for class to start.

"Hello," the teacher said, somewhat startling Erin. "My name is Ms. Patty. Feel welcome to choose any seat to sit in."

Erin quickly turned to the teacher, who was a lady that looked to be in her 40s.

Erin hesitantly spoke, "Hi." She walked closer to the teacher. "Hey, um, did you get my email?"

Ms. Patty's eyes lit up, "Oh! You must be Erin, right? Don't worry, I got your message. I made sure to change what I have to make sure you feel comfortable here."

Erin felt relieved, "Thank you so much."

Ms. Patty smiled, "You're so welcome! If anyone gives you any trouble, know that you can come to me about it, all right?"

Erin smiled back, "I will. Thanks again."

Erin then sat down at an empty table. The class slowly filled up as the time ticked forward. Her table remained mostly empty with just one other person there. Erin felt too scared to speak to anyone new, though.

Class started and everything was fairly normal. Ms. Patty took attendance, talked about the syllabus, what to expect from the class, other things that teachers say on the first day of school. Then she asked everyone to introduce themselves by saying their name and a hobby of theirs. Erin started to feel tense again. She was rehearsing what she would say, what tone she would say it in, and was making sure it was perfect. Ms. Patty then called on her.

Erin hesitantly got up, "Hi, my name is Erin, and I like to draw."

She quickly sat back down. Everyone else in class was silent. She looked around to see some confused looks, some who were interested in her hobby, and those who weren't paying attention. She honestly preferred the last group to the rest. Class ended shortly after that. She quickly got up and gathered her things. She'd rather not stay in one place for too long.

Her second block was close to her first class, so finding it wasn't difficult by any means. She asked the teacher, Mr. Roberts, about the email that she sent to him. The teacher didn't say much, but it seemed like he was cool with it. He taught social studies, and he immediately started teaching after class started. History wasn't Erin's favorite subject, but Mr. Roberts taught it well. The whole class period was fine and nothing notable happened, which was excellent for Erin.

Erin's third block was math, and it was a bit far from her other classes, so it took her a while longer to get there. She had to rush a little to get there and was a bit out of breath when she walked through the door. She started to walk up to the teacher, Mr. Walton.

She started, "Hi, did you—"

Ring.

The bell rang as she was trying to talk to him.

"Sorry, we can talk later. Please take your seat," Mr. Walton said.

Erin felt she had to talk to him about the email, but she didn't want to get in trouble and sat down at the last empty seat next to a boy. She didn't know who the boy sitting next to her was, but he gave off a bad aura.

The teacher stood at the front of the class behind his podium; he was holding the attendance sheet. He called off the names in a rather monotone voice like a robot. Her name was getting close to being called. She was mentally rehearsing saying *here* as it drew nearer. Her name was next. Mr. Walton spoke and …

It wasn't the right name.

Erin felt her heart drop. This was the last thing she wanted to happen today. She had planned everything — made sure this wouldn't happen. She felt herself tearing up. The room felt like it had eyes, all of which were watching her. She was in another dimension. She was fighting off warriors, archers shooting arrows at her, and she was alone.

Mr. Walton looked around the room. He repeated the name. Another arrow. He looked around again. She couldn't surrender. She was fighting with herself. They were both fighting to give up or stand strong: *But what would that say about us? We can't be marked absent though. Can you even take any more hits? How many arrows until some real damage is done?*

She slowly raised her white flag. "Here…"

The other students looked at her. Confused, hateful, mean looks from what she could see. She couldn't handle this. Every archer shot at once and hit her in the heart. The boy next to her understood well what she was. It felt like her father all over again. She kept her head close to the desk. Too many arrows. Too much damage. Too much self-hatred.

Class went by really fast, and Erin barely heard the bell when it ended. She couldn't really focus after.

She left the room and started heading off to lunch. The hallway was mostly empty, as others had either made it to the cafeteria or had class at this time.

She was stopped in her tracks, though, when she was called a word she was never called before. He shot an arrow at her. She knew it was a slur, but she had never felt the effect it could have against someone.

She turned around to see two boys, one of which she had sat next to in her last class. She turned back around and walked faster to get to lunch. He said it again. Another arrow.

"Didn't you hear me?" he asked. "It's just what you are, and you will never be a—"

"Didn't you hear to mind your own business?" a voice responded.

Erin was shocked when she saw a girl now standing beside her. A fellow comrade? Who was she?

The boys seemed annoyed and walked off.

The girl looked at Erin. "Hey, are you alright?"

"Yeah, thank you," Erin replied quietly.

The girl didn't seem to believe Erin, but she continued, "I'm Lynn. I was, uh, in your last class."

Erin started tearing up. So many people knew now, and they were bound to tell others.

Lynn saw her tears. "No — hey, it's alright. I'm so sorry you were outed like that, and no one else had a right to know about it unless you said it yourself."

Erin looked to her, surprised to hear what she had to say.

Lynn continued, "Know that I and so many others support you for who you are. You aren't alone."

Lynn smiled. Erin smiled back. The two walked to lunch together.

Spectrum

by Hannah Wolf

Why are we symbolized with the rainbow?

We saw the world through monochrome lenses,
Until we reached inside our souls and discovered colors we'd never seen.
These pigments made us want to shine, for how could we hide our multicolored hearts?
Red by yellow by lavender and cyan,
Those hidden hues began to blossom.

The black-and-white world looked down upon our diverse hearts
And pretended to be colorblind.

"Were we not shining brightly enough?" we asked
As we lit our colors aflame,
But instead the intransigents jumbled us into a muddy stew.
Our colors began to fade,
Warp,
Break,
Pinken with the mark of the lowest shame.

More ashes than fire remained of us.

This is why we are a rainbow:
Because the world knows our colors once more.
So until I can stand proud without fear of my flame extinguished,
Until I no longer have to mention "my, um, significant other" with a sweet smile
And hope they don't detect my fearful undertone,
Until I can hold her hand and never consider
That someone may break us for their petty enjoyment,

Or force us apart because they can't bear to see love in its purest form,
The seven-colored ribbon spans a cloudy sky
And brings hope when spilling rain blocks the sun.

The entire spectrum, in that moment,
Leads the broken to their hard-fought place in the light.

Thought Process

by Zoey Plytas

She comes up to me in a rush in a —

please don't mind my sentences that don't flow don't make sense don't
I don't really know how to talk
to pretty girls the way maybe I should or shouldn't or should
or and so

I choke up when I feel things things like
the way she throws her head back when she laughs and I can see her canines
and her her
hair bounces around her head and I bet it's softer than her voice saying my
name and
will she even let me get close to her
closer than straight knees
on crisscross applesauced knees under the willow
close close
I mean not clingy close but like

close enough to count the freckles on her cheeks
there have to be at least like twenty
million
I kind of want to I mean if she lets me
touch her cheeks to read them
like we did in elementary school with the whole follow the words on the page
as we read a story about a girl who
made everyone so happy
and my stomach tickles and my finger follows the freckled letters and —

I don't know I just want her near me like
how can someone be so right for me and just right for the

world in that sort of wholesome righteous fall in love with me way —

and actually
I'm scared of falling in love
giving all of myself to someone as amazing and wonderful and beautiful as her her her
because I am a girl
who has too much eyebrow and laugh
not enough charm and grace
this girl is everything I need
but does she need me
really need me
like really

and I'm so scared but it doesn't seem as scary if

really

I wouldn't mind if if

she takes me by the hand
arm around my waist
firm warm hand on my waist
and I blush
as we go back around the hall to get my backpack
because I forgot it
when she offered to walk me to class
because we were standing in the other hall
together
and I got so caught up in
together I forgot
So I blush

as she laughs at me
but not in a a laughing at me type of way but more of in a —

is she going to let me in and make me hers and and

she does
she really
she does
even with my shaky hands and
I'm probably sweating
and how can something so great happen to me
me
of all the crummy people in the world
and what if I mess this up and I am so afraid of what happens next and I
hug her
because she opens her arms to me
because I told her make me yours
and I blush
and I hug her
just hug her
because I have never been kissed anyone
yet.

She's Not

by Rachael Potter

Content warning: suicide

She's not, she's not, she can't.
She swore she wouldn't, she swore it.
But now,
Lying in front of me, the wall a grotesque painting of red.
I'm afraid to touch her.
I hover over her, my falling tears dripping down her face.
She seems at peace, more so than she ever was in life.
But there's something missing from her.
Her light.
And what about me?
She left me here.
Alone.
She's selfish.
Do you hear this, wherever you ended up?
You're selfish!
But what about me?
I was selfish, too.
I should have tried harder when she needed me.
I should have held her when she was afraid and lost.
I should have.
I should have done so much.
But now the paint is drying.
The artist is going cold.
Maybe if I hold her tight enough she'll grow warm again.
Maybe she'll reach up to wipe the tears away.
And tell me that she would never leave me alone.
Leave me alone in a world so cruel.
A world that would torture an angel.

Maybe my angel is waiting for me.
Maybe she got her wings back.
Maybe I should go find her.
Maybe I should add my own painting to the walls.

Insufficient Cause for Reason

by Caitlynn Fleming

He wakes up in the morning but life is still the same.
Not flat enough, not tall enough, not man enough.
Not man enough
What a joke
Because that's all he is in the eyes of the public
Someone playing dress up
A child who wants attention
Someone so starved for affection
But what did he ever do
Other than ask for your respect
He says he
You then reply she
You say stop pretending little girl
You think you know it all
But you don't
You
Don't
He picks up his phone to pass the time
One message
Two messages
Three messages
He quickly shuts off his phone in fear
Fear of the ridicule he might receive
Fear of the hate for himself
Fear of purposeful misgendering
But what did he do to deserve this
This war not only with himself but the world as well
Respect him
Respect her
Respect them

Respect everyone you see
The daily battle of living with yourself is hard enough
He goes to bed
Still in fear
Still sad
Still frustrated
At the world
And himself

Over the Fireworks

by Lisa Ing

Blair watched as the fireworks display began, the explosions of color in the night sky illuminating the balcony. Akio sat next to him, with an expression full of wonder as his eyes fixated on the beautiful patterns that emerged in the air.

Without losing sight of the fireworks, Akio asked, "Remember when we were kids and our families took us to this same fireworks display for New Year's?"

Blair took a moment to recall that night, but the truth was he didn't remember much besides Akio's amazed expression as he ignited a fireworks sparkler to provide light after the display ended.

***

"Your sparkler is so cool, Blair!" Akio exclaimed. "And pretty, too."

Blair huffed with pride, satisfied that his sparkler burned brighter than the rest. "Of course it's cool! But my sparkler isn't 'pretty' — it's deadly!"

Akio giggled. "I think pretty things can be deadly too."

Blair pondered for a moment and looked up from his sparkler, deciding that maybe "pretty" wasn't so bad of a word after all as he took in the gaze of wonder before him. Blair's breath hitched.

Akio sat in front of him, with a face full of stars as he watched the sparks fly from Blair's grasp. The yellow light emitted from the sparks illuminated Akio's face just right, making the young toddler appear even softer before Blair.

"The light coming from the sparks is so pretty," Akio cooed.

Yeah, Blair thought. His eyes never strayed from the boy before him, engulfed in a blanket of light, *Pretty*.

***

It felt like lifetimes ago, thinking about it now. He didn't understand what he felt that night, and rightfully so. Blair wasn't a "feelings" person, so he never imagined that he would look at another person, nevermind Akio, in that way. Despite their many childhood sleepovers and playdates, the two boys had grown apart during their middle school years. The wedge between them was further deepened when they developed separate interests and friend groups. To the outside world, it seemed as if the two boys had grown apart, maturing beyond the foundations built upon their youth.

However, one thing stayed constant throughout the years: Blair was inherently a competitive person and thrived off of surpassing others in everything he participated in. Over the years, the only one who could keep up with him was Akio, whose work ethic and determination rivaled Blair's talent. Their rivalry connected them during middle school, despite growing apart from each other. Rather, they pushed each other to grow into the best version of themselves, with the two boys emerging from middle school as the top two students in academics.

Now as high school students, Akio had taken an interest in rekindling their friendship, inviting him to hang out, enjoying the nostalgia of things they used to do together. As reluctant as Blair was to admit it, he was glad that Akio had a more daily role in his life now. Not that he'd ever tell Akio that, of course.

His thoughts were interrupted by a muffled "Blair? Earth to Blair …" effectively snapping Blair out of his trip down memory lane.

Akio watched him with concern. "You never answered my question. Do you remember when we watched the fireworks here when we were little?"

"Oh, right," Blair said, mentally slapping himself before he nodded in confirmation.

Akio brightened with that damn pretty smile and turned to face the edge of the balcony, gazing at the fireworks once again. "I thought that the fact that we're both standing here together says a lot about our improvement."

Blair raised an eyebrow, prompting Akio to elaborate.

"I mean, I'm glad that … I'm glad that we got to the point that we could do this again. Being friends, I mean," Akio stuttered, turning away from Blair as he said so.

As Blair watched another firework boom in the sky, he grinned. "I'm glad too."

However, the sound of the explosion completely masked his voice, preventing Akio from hearing him.

"What was that, Blair?"

Blair huffed. He could only be soft for so long before he reverted to his normal demeanor, rough and mean around the edges. "Didn't say anything, Akio. Even if I did, you would have been too deaf to hear anyways. Get your ears checked."

"Well maybe that's because I spend so much time near your yelling," Akio teased as he nudged Blair's shoulder. Blair's stomach erupted in butterflies at the contact, making him blanch inside at how soft the boy made him feel. However, it did give him an idea.

Blair waited for the next firework to ignite, watching it rise in the night sky. The very moment the firework erupted, Blair murmured, barely above a whisper, "I'm glad we're friends again."

Akio sat a few feet beside him, unaware of Blair's musing over the sound of the fireworks. A resounding series of explosions shook the balcony, illuminating the atmosphere.

Blair seized his chance once again with a murmur, "I want to be your main rival, always." Two other explosions, blasting off within seconds of each other. "Thank you, for never giving up on me."

Blair continued like this for the remainder of the show, whispering all the things that echoed in his heart but he hadn't yet the courage to say out loud. Eventually, he found protection in his cover of fireworks and Akio's obliviousness and began to become more daring. Despite how confident he normally was, the palms of his hands became clammy and brewing with nervous energy, quivering in the cool night air.

BOOM!

"I want to spend more time with you."

BOOM!

"You're everything to me."

BOOM!

"You're beautiful."

With each passing firework, the compliments transformed into something that Blair didn't know what to make of. He had never put much thought into his feelings for the boy next to him, but the words flowing out of his mouth seem to indicate otherwise. Thoughts like these began to surface at the oddest of moments while trying to recover their friendship. Like right now, for example. Blair couldn't quite name the feeling in his chest that often accompanied these thoughts, it was foreign, and yet it wasn't unwelcome either.

Oblivious to the storm that brewed in Blair's chest, Akio noticed his quivering hands, and raised an eyebrow with a silent question, *You okay?*

He was too observant for his own good sometimes, Blair cursed. "The hell are you looking at?"

Akio eyed his sparks with concern. "You're acting nervous. Did something happen?"

A rush of blood rose up Blair's averted face, painting the tips of his ears red. He looked up to retaliate and stopped when he took in the sight before him. A wave of déjà vu washed over him as he saw how the light from fireworks softened Akio's features. He observed how the aforementioned light reflected off of his eyes, his hair illuminated with the bright fireworks igniting in the distant background, gone unnoticed. Blair vaguely noticed that the explosions of color in the sky got brighter and brighter, increasing in intensity as his heart bumped erratically out of tune in his chest until —

"I think I love you."

BOOM!

Blair stiffened, his back ramrod straight as he mentally scolded himself. What an idiot he was, to mess up something so simple so easily with just a slip of his tongue.

Although it was barely over a whisper, Akio had surely heard it. He snapped up to look at the boy before him with wide eyes of disbelief. The sea of silence between them was deafening, as if the fireworks ceased fire just for this very moment, time slowing down.

The silence was broken by Akio first, "W…what was that, Blair?"

Blood rushed to Blair's face once again as he launched himself away from Akio. "I … It's nothing," he said with averted eyes.

"Blair," Akio stated firmly, "What was that you said just now?" His sharp gaze was locked onto him now, making Blair want to crawl into a hole and die of embarrassment.

But Blair wasn't a coward. He'd triumphed over every competition he had the care to compete in, surely he could look Akio in the eye. Plain and simple.

He forced himself up to face Akio, his heart skipping more beats than he thought was healthy. Well, Blair reasoned, Akio already heard him, so might as well not turn back now.

He took a moment to recall how to articulate words and whispered, "I think I love you."

The fireworks show must have ended by then, Blair thought, based on the prolonged and uninterrupted silence that spanned between him and Akio's widened eyes. Blair turned away again, facing away from the other young man almost as if to avoid seeing his reaction. He hated the silence. His breath suddenly became sparse in his chest, and forced his eyes to the ground that he so wished would swallow him whole.

Blair interrupted the silent tension with a curt, "Just forget it, this doesn't change anything—"

He was interrupted by a series of sniffles coming from Akio, whose smile underneath his tears seemed to serve to feed his alarm. Blair never imagined that Akio would be crying as he ripped his heart out and cut off their friendship.

"Blair," Akio said with a shaky voice through his tears, "I love you too."

Blair's eyes snapped back up to gawk at Akio, trying to discern if this was some sort of sick prank — and Akio's arms were wrapped around his back. Blair stood there numb for a moment in shock, finally processed that Akio was hugging him, and slowly raised his arms and wrapped them around Akio's waist. He shuffled awkwardly to adjust and properly support both of their weight, and sighed into the crook of Akio's neck as Akio's tears inevitably stained his shirt.

After a minute, Blair asked, "Is it true? That you love me?"

He felt Akio nod into his now tear-stained shirt and felt himself relax into Akio's embrace. "W-why do you think I'm crying this much?" Akio sniffed. "I'm really happy, Blair." With that, he peered up to look at the blond through his tears. Blair felt himself drawn closer and closer to Akio, their foreheads nearly touching at the almost gravitational pull. Akio seemed to understand and leaned up into Blair. Unfortunately, his excitement got the best of him, and he shot up with a bit too much force, causing them to bump noses. The surprise of the impact caught Blair off guard, and only served to make him even more flustered than he already was, the tips of his ears turning pink.

"Oh my god," Akio wheezed as he nuzzled into the crook of Blair's neck in embarrassment, "I just ruined our first kiss, Blair I am so sorry—"

"S-shut up." Blair sputtered, praying that it was too dark for Akio to notice the blush that was starting to make its way up his face. Despite this, he continued to nuzzle into the crook of Akio's neck, and Akio returned the gesture.

"This is nice," Akio said with a sigh, and Blair could only grumble in agreement as he tightened his embrace.

Akio giggled as an unexpected series of explosions rocked the balcony, a grand finale to such an eventful night, startling Blair. Glaring at the other boy, Blair stalked across the balcony and ignited a handheld fireworks sparkler, continuing a tradition set by the two boys all those years ago. He slumped beside Akio and he held his sparkler away from his body as if to avoid burning Akio if he got too close.

Their foreheads rested against each other as Akio smiled in the illumination of Blair's sparks, remarking, "The sparks are so beautiful, Blair."

Blair's eyes never strayed from the boy before him, melting at his touch and how beautiful Akio looked when illuminated like this.

"Yeah," Blair said. "Beautiful."

Queer Thoughts and Questions About Them

by Pheebi C.

1. blue lace dress

you don't have nightmares often, but when you do, they scare the shit out of you,
and when it's over and you wake up you call me saying,
sorry, it's 4 in the morning, it's too early for this, but you're scared of how successfully your imagination works against you in your sleep
I say it's okay.
you keep talking,
saying how the black shadows of the trees look like stitches on a blue lace dress through your window, about how pretty that dress would look on me, about the few birds that have woken up and are singing to each other, about oh gosh now it's 5 and you can see the colors on the stitches of my dress

•••

you keep talking and you're half asleep and your eyes can barely focus and neither of us can think straight, and you don't touch on the nightmare, you never do
and I don't ask because even if you've never said so I know it's the same as the others.

••

it's 5:30 now and you've calmed down enough to want to go back to sleep, or maybe your stomach is still a little queasy and your heart hasn't quite stopped running from the dream yet, but either way you don't want me to feel this in the morning and you say thanks and sorry again and see you later and then click, you're gone.

•

but I do feel it later, because I lay awake for another half an hour, wondering why can't you tell me what's bothering you? is it me? are you worried about something? about us? please why can't you tell me I want to help
and then I roll over and realize I'm just as bad as you, that I can't tell you or anyone what I'm worried about but

maybe one day,
I'll be wearing a blue lace dress and it'll be 4 in the morning and the birds are chirping, and I'll be coming to you for help, when my heart stops and I can't breathe and I want just to feel safe
and maybe one day we'll both have the guts to spill everything to each other, maybe one day we'll both stop waking up too early in the morning and being scared and maybe one day, I'll be wearing a blue lace dress and I'll look pretty in it and neither of us will associate it with nightmares and worries.

2. between the lines
you are small and you are at your big cousin's wedding.
you can't really see them, so your mind wanders a bit.
what will you do on your wedding? will you have to stand up and talk?
but these thoughts are forced. you don't want that. you don't want a wedding.
but maybe, maybe if i meet the right guy, you think.

kids are nosy. they ask lots of questions, and they like playing games that ask lots of questions.
"truth or dare?" they scream.
"truth," you know what they're gonna ask,
"tell me who your crush is!" you know they won't believe you,
"dare."
"i dare you to tell me who your crush is!"
"fine. i don't have one." but what can you say?
"liar!"
you were bored. really, really bored.

you are small and you are in a car with your best friend. he is a boy.
you'll grow up and get married one day, his mom says.
"no. i don't want that."
her voice merges with your mother's.

"yes. you'll change your mind when you're older. i bet you'll want children too."
you're not really friends anymore. you both grew up and neither of you need a babysitter.
it's fine. you weren't that great of a friend anyway, nevertheless one for him to marry.

those kids haven't gotten any less nosier.
"are you?" they ask.
"am i what?" you say.
"gay?"
the question catches you off guard. only a second passes by, but it's a second nonetheless.
it's none of your business, you tell them.

a big flag hangs in your room. your dad put it there for you; he doesn't know what it means.
it's okay. he's old. he's not from here.
your mother tells you how good of an ally you must be. she doesn't try to make it her business.

you are at your house. your best friend is with you.
it's late, you're both tired.
"what are we?"
she's silent for a moment. she doesn't know.
you don't know either. that's why you asked.

you don't know how to feel. you don't know what you want,
and it should be a simple answer. it used to be.
you've felt it since you were little, but now… something's changed.
the people you knew changed, and you changed with them.

there's more to it than you thought.

you can't tell where the line between friends end and where the other one starts.
it's complicated. it sucks, because christ why can't it just be simple?

you might as well just be a dog chasing its own tail. every question just goes around in circles.

what is it supposed to feel like?
what feeling am i feeling right now?
it is the right one?
do i want it to be the right one?

i don't know.
it's something.
maybe.
i don't know.

it's nice, you guess. but it's not what everyone else is thinking,
it's not what you're thinking.

it's right down in the middle, between friends and lovers.
i think they'd look at you like you were crazy,
but not all feelings can be described with words, and you're not nosy enough to find one that fits.

I don't have answers to all your questions,
and I'm fine with that, really.

I just wish everyone else was.

3. her

it was raining
when we sat in the courtyard talking about our dreams.

she tells me how she robbed a bank, how she drove to a beautiful mountain, how people she loved lived and died in her subconscious. she asks about me and my dreams, but i don't tell her that her hair holds every one of them.

she is beautiful,
and so is her smile and the nights we'd stay up talking about our existence and all the things that had happened to us, that were happening to us, all the things that made her feel not so beautiful.

we talked about our dreams — our plans for the future, as if we had any control over it. i wanted to go to college, she wanted to take a road trip to florida. she doesn't know if she'd come back, and to tell the truth i don't know what i'd do if she didn't.

the moon was out on those nights,
as clear and lucid as the fears of losing her. i didn't tell her about those either.

the days have flashed by since we first came to meet,
and I love her a little more everyday.

she isn't perfect,
scars aren't pretty.
but even the moon has its flaws, every mark and missing piece has a story, and i stay up on those nights when the moon isn't full, when it's missing a part of itself and i think
god, what did i do to deserve someone like this? what did i do to deserve someone so beautiful?

and she is. she is beautiful.
she's not perfect,
but when her eyelashes held the stars and her fingers held mine, the moment was,

it was perfect and it was beautiful and i'd give everything to find it again.

You Were My First Love

by Sam K.

Lips like raspberry, hands like silk.
Deep brown eyes, small smile lines.
Your face was like a work of art; I wanted to admire more.
Our moments were brief, like a gust of wind.
I took in the moments whenever they came;
You made me believe in love.

But moments are only moments, as a wise man once said;
For moments were never enough for you.
You wanted more, a greed I could not indulge.
My safety was my priority.
We drifted away and the lights faded.
The moments were just an earthquake; hurt was our aftershock.
After the shock, we came back down from the puppy love high.
I had to say I love you.
I had to say I love you.
I had to show I loved you.

but I can't. not if I want to live.

So maybe our paths will cross again; maybe not.
To this day I still eat raspberries and think of you.
I love you.
Maybe one day I can show you that.

Senses

by Omar Escudero

Content warning: abuse

do you think he can feel it
cuts on my hands
do you think he can feel it
calluses on my feet
do you think he can feel it
moonlight washed over my face
do you think he felt it
when he snapped your heart like a twig

do you think he can see it
when the fireflies glow
do you think he can see it
brighter than the headlights
do you think he saw it
when the twinkle in your eyes fades

do you think he could hear it
the wind, whistling sweet nothings
do you think he could hear it
i sing back, my voice breaking like branches
do you think he heard it
when he hit you so hard you felt your ears ring

do you think he could taste it
the humid june air
do you think he could taste it
the fear radiating from you
do you think he tasted it

what it was like to be freed

though i'm broken from the pain
i still love you the same
even when we're apart
the moon lights my way

A Reading from the Book of Sappho

by Brianna Cunliffe

I have never heard anything but love
spoken from that pulpit
yet it is the pulpit
so ornate, solid and ancient
no room for me in its divine tapestries

I have loved this church
with its scent of incense and sea breeze
ashes and wine
I have loved its red-brown bricks and cool stone floor
the stained-glass casting colors on my face
a flash of seasons, of
a wide-eyed toddler, clutching at the rainbows in the air,
joining in a high shout of
'allelula, allelula!'
(the congregation chuckles)
a young girl with holy sawdust in her mouth
(and the first taste of wine on her tongue)
a girl stepping to the altar to sing, her eyes catching those same rainbows
as she leads the song of
'alleluia, alleluia'
(the congregation smiles)

Despite what I have felt about God
I have always loved that dome
all weightlessness and light
have loved its priest for his shortness and baldness
his kindness and faith
like the blind and lovely owl who sings for a dawn only he can see

And it is here, with the smiling saints of my youth
letting their light be mine
with two centuries of flawed goodwill woven into the bricks
that I saw myself in white,
loved ones' footsteps against marble floor
soaring skyward in varied tones
as will the 'alleluia, alleluia'
just as so many times before
and with the faith of a child I knew
that one day this place I have loved
would seal my greatest love
and in the light of its face we would become one

And yet as the years went by the light bared
something in me some would call unholy
and as I sung I felt it move in me
the white of my dress, the look on his face
obscured by the sudden flare of colorful light

these saints of my youth and their irony
for now that dream is made a coin
and one side is dark as the pulpit's wood
beside the golden cross

Their light plays upon my eyes and they call to me
'little saint, you, the singer of hymns,
do you believe in his love?'
and I cannot answer but to say
'all I know of love
is this flawed, lovely dome under a sea-wet sky
and a girl with eyes more holy than the host.'

and the saints of my youth are smiling, but they are hard to see
behind the specters of long-robed men sickening with gold and old age
who say there is no room for me
in this place I love

And I will not under this dome be knit,
soul in soul
with the earthly heaven I hope to find
in whoever sees in me a love worth chasing
and I will mourn this
I cannot do otherwise.
and even as I sing aloud the
'alleluia, alleluia'
it is a cry against the rancid myth which stretches
languorous and vile
across the centuries
crowding out the grace I have always found in this place
leaving no room in its rafters
for my love to roost.

Bury Your Dead(name)

by Keegan Thoranin

Burying you wasn't like burying a hatchet.
Though we've thrown our fair share of sticks and stones
While our identities tangled
Like alley cats in battle,
It felt more like putting you to rest.
Burying you was like saying goodbye.
For those that leave you — good or bad — are never gone.
It was a respite from each other's company,
Though it'd be a lie to say I missed it.
You were the seed our parents harvested,
Plucked at birth and patterned in pink.
But nobody ever blames a seed for growing,
And neither should we.
And so, as I lay you in this soil,
The earth I once thought cold and unwelcome,
Let the ground I till for you,
Be our new beginning,
Because you are not a shell of who I was.
No.
You are an acorn.
A seed with a sprout that broke out,
Young and green, fragile,
But still kicking.
So, down you go.
Your new home,
May our branches grow safely and strong.
I don't worry if people may have known you,
Cause, after all,
Nobody ever looks at a tree,
And thinks of the seed that was sown.

Evan(geline)

by Anon Zephyr

The night is alive with the calls of bullfrogs and crickets, a warm summer night reminiscent of the last time the triplets stood at the steps of Montebellia High School. The land hasn't changed much in the decade they've been gone —there's a new Dairy Queen down the block, and some new sororities and fraternities have popped up on the university campus across the street, but the corner deli is still open and selling Emily's favorite green tea ginger ale, the university's food court still houses Ethan's pizzeria of choice for Friday lunches, even the loose brick in the sidewalk Evangeline used to trip on no matter how careful she was is still there, much to her chagrin.

What has changed is them: Emily is wearing more makeup than her conservative teenage style would ever dream of, Ethan grew a beard and has crow's feet from laughing so much over the years, and Evangeline is wearing a dress. Of all the changes, though, the strength of their bond is not one of them, and the triplets are ready to conquer Montebellia for a second time.

They walk in, and all of a sudden it's like they're back in high school, eighteen and dumb, running through the hallways to spite teachers, cracking jokes at the lunch table their friends had claimed and maintained for four years, cursing every time the fire alarm went off in the middle of class, pretending to pay attention in the history class they all shared during senior year, even though they were really doodling and writing in the margins of their notebooks. There are the senior steps where they had staked out in the mornings as they charged their phones and scrambled to finish homework. There's the bathroom where Emily first had her period freshmen year in the middle of biology — while the class studied reproduction, no less. There's the stairwell where Ethan had stolen his first kiss in his sophomore year with a junior girl named Hannah Savay. And there's the Commons where their former classmates would congregate, the same Commons where Evangeline first wore a dress.

This time, the Commons are dressed up in finery that had originally been intended for a hotel ballroom that had cancelled on the alumni the week prior. In the panic of searching for a new location, the Montebellia Class of 2008 had decided to reunite at their high school. It was then that Emily, junior class president, had proposed the theme of nostalgia. It's apparent in the music flowing through the cafeteria-turned-dancehall as the triplets put their bags and jackets in the coat check and repeat their past habit of racing each other to the refreshment table as soon as they're situated. Ethan wins the race this time, laughing with his sisters as he hands them each a cookie.

Once they've had their sugar fill, the triplets at last get their first look at the dance floor, where their classmates talk, trading memories and stories, and dance, letting their hips sway to the rhythm of One Direction and Gwen Stefani, Soulja Boy and Green Day. Emily hears her name and finds her old group of friends, a gaggle of mostly girls who happened to be friends with other girls and boys, some of whom were friends and still are friends with Ethan and Evangeline, a friend group that resembles a web of close friends and besties and acquaintances and couples and ex-couples and study partners and lunch buddies. Emily squeals and runs over, hugging them all as they start chatting about college and jobs and the families some of them have started, from children to pets to partners.

Meanwhile, Ethan and Evangeline wait on the fringes of the group — as much as they love these girls, their crowd had been mostly guys. The first of their friends the siblings see is Christopher Hopkins. He's spinning his wife Fina around as they laugh and dance. Ethan calls his name and the two turn towards them with a cry of surprise at the difference between high-school-Ethan and just-got-his-life-together-after-college-Ethan.

"Ethan, my man!" Chris greets, pulling his friend in for a hug right away. "How's it been going?" He pauses, studying Evangeline, who holds her breath, resisting the urge to flatten out her dress. "Is this Ashley?" Ethan's confused for a second before he realizes Chris is referring to Evangeline. Her brother glances at her, allowing her to respond.

"Actually," she says as she tucks a loose strand of hair behind her ear, "I'm Evangeline." She waits just long enough for the nerves from earlier that night to bubble up as Chris processes her words, the recognition at last hitting him.

"Evan?" he asks. "Wait, no, sorry — Evangeline?"

She laughs nervously, nodding shyly.

"I didn't even recognize you! How have you been? I didn't realize you've started wearing dresses again. You look nice," Chris blurts in one breath until Fina taps his shoulder gently, reminding her husband to breathe. Evangeline's heart is hammering despite her introductions going far better than she planned; she can feel it pounding at her ribcage with the force of an ocean wave, though it doesn't seem that anybody can see how skittish she feels inside.

"I've been travelling, mostly," she answers. "Freelance photography can send you to the most amazing places. I came back a few weeks ago from this little village on the Irish coast. You'll be able to see the photos soon. I'll send you a copy of the magazine," she rambles, feeling the apprehension slowly ebb away as she settles back into her element. Photography and dresses are her comfort zone — public engagements are not. She feels something tug at her arm and sees Ethan trying to get her attention.

"I think I see someone you might want to dance with," Ethan chuckles, jutting his head in the direction of—

Austin Moore. Her high school — and by the way her heart is fluttering, current — crush. Her face lights up like a firework as Chris and Fina's gazes follow the direction of Ethan's attention. Chris laughs devilishly, remembering all the lunch periods spent whining about how Austin could never like her or how her major crush was just not going away, much to her despair. He's still as handsome as ever (probably even more), and Evangeline could still happily stare into his lime green eyes for ages.

"Someone's got hearts in their eyes," Chris whispers in a teasing tone, relishing the fierce blush on her cheeks. "I can't believe you still haven't gotten over Austin."

"I had boyfriends in college!" Evangeline snorts at that. "Maybe I still think he's cute, but that's — Chris, what are you doing?"

Chris is waving his hand, trying to get Austin's attention.

"No, don't you dare—"

"Hey, Austin!" Chris yells across the room as Evangeline groans. "C'mere! How you doing, man?"

Austin turns and sees the group, grinning as he heads over to them. For a moment, Evangeline swears the air heats up around her as his gaze falls upon her.

"Good luck, Evangeline," Chris murmurs to her as Austin approaches them.

His gaze is on her. She can't break it; she's entranced — and, yeah, her crush has definitely remained over the years.

"Hey." Austin's voice is as quiet as ever, but since she last saw him almost ten years ago, it's dropped an octave and resonates in the air like the quiet song of hummingbirds. "It's awesome to see you, Chris, Fina."

In typical fashion, the two men clasp hands and side-hug one another, a tradition Evangeline never understood.

Austin asks, "Ethan, what you've been up to?" Her brother responds vaguely, mentioning his girlfriend Ashley and their recent trip to Thailand to meet her grandparents.

Austin faces Evangeline and she's never felt more nervous in life, not even when she was scaling the side of a mountain for a close-up of a couple goats.

"I'm going to go get some more snacks, I'll see you later," Chris says as Fina follows him, signing goodbye as she winks at Evangeline with a smirk.

"It's been a while, Evan," Austin mumbles, still awkward and shy. A sharp, twisted feeling, like a punch to the gut, hits her, leaving a taste like bile on her tongue. "You look really pretty. Lapis is definitely your color."

The nausea is rising slowly, crawling to its climax, and she finds herself unable to speak. Out of the corner of her eyes, she sees Ethan step up, shooting her a quick look, a silent promise that everything will be alright.

He whispers in Austin's ear, whose cheeks color fiercely as he registers Ethan's meaning.

"Oh. Oh." Austin glances back guiltily at Evangeline. "Oh, sheesh, I'm sorry, Evangeline. I didn't know — I didn't mean to hurt you," he apologizes sincerely. "Sorry."

She's not sure what exactly to say, besides the fact that Austin has always left her tongue-tied. "It's — um, it's okay. This is my first time back here after coming out, and transitioning, and all that jazz. But — but thanks for the apology." She has half the mind to scream at her stutters, berating herself mentally.

"I feel like an idiot," Austin laughs, rubbing the back of his neck sheepishly.

"You kind of are," Ethan chimes in, grunting in pain as Evangeline elbows her brother. "Ow, okay, I get the idea, I'll leave you two alone!" He's laughing and Evangeline knows he's off to tell Emily everything, and by the time they've all gone back home for the night, Emily and Ethan will be interrogating her to the ends beyond earth. She half-wishes he would come back.

"Brothers, am I right?" Austin says with a lopsided grin. His gaze is less curious now. It's soft and gentle, like the fabric of her blanket back in her apartment halfway across the country, and it makes her heart stutter. She knows she's safe, that Austin meant it when he said he had no malintent. In his gaze, she can see the future she had always fantasized of having but had been too shy to make a reality of. "Sorry again for … all that." He pauses, wringing his hands. "Your dress really is pretty, though — you're really pretty and oh, sheesh, I didn't mean to say that aloud."

Evangeline giggles. Austin's smile wavers and she can see the apprehension behind his green eyes.

Austin starts, "There's something—something I should probably tell you."

"You can tell me anything," she blurts just a tad too earnestly.

"I've … oh, sheesh, how do I put this?" He laughs nervously, sharing Evangeline's anxiety. "Y'see, I've kind of, maybe, had feelings for you and maybe I still have them?"

The world must've ended, there's nothing but the sound of her heartbeat and the echoes of Austin's words. All at once, reality restarts and her heart is ringing in her ears; the butterflies in her stomach have been released from their habitat and are flying throughout her veins.

"No way," she whispers, her mouth quirking up into a grin. "You know I've waited ten years to hear that?"

She takes his hand and squeezes it, gleeful laughter spilling past her lips. Austin chuckles once, twice, and soon he's joined her in the disbelieving laughter of star-crossed lovers.

He kisses her knuckles gently, sending another burst of lightning through her body and a blush across her face, and pulls her towards the dancing crowd. "Would you want to get coffee at Beanie's tomorrow?"

She grins. "Wouldn't miss it for the world."

They dance the rest of the night, laughing like everybody else, catching up with their friends and classmates, swiping quick bites of each other's food when the other isn't looking. Ethan and Emily find their sister sitting in the corner with Austin, her head on his shoulder as she talks about pride. Evangeline goes home with a new number in her phone, an unstoppable beam on her face, and a promise for tomorrow. The now early morning hours are alive, for sure —they are alive with the sounds of the calls of bullfrogs, the chapters of life, and the unfolding love of Evangeline.

Bathroom

by Sasha Piacek

I feel the pressure rising in my lower abdomen, consequently I feel my heart sink
There's a million thoughts racing through my head now:
'Can I hold it until I'm home?'
'Is there a single stall around here?'
'Why did I drink so much water today?'
'Maybe the bathrooms are empty… God I hope so'
My legs are losing feeling, my hands trembling, I can hear my heart beating faster and harder
My stomach drops as I approach the door, the sign reads "Ladies' Room"
I enter
With a sigh of relief, the room is empty
I stop in front of the mirror and examine every crease and line
Again my mind is racing:
'Why are you this way?'
'Couldn't you have been born differently?'
'Your hair is too feminine'
'Your figure is too curvy'
'Everybody thinks you're faking it'
I turn away before the thoughts get worse — before I hate myself more than anybody ever could
The cold porcelain sends goosebumps down my legs
The creak of the bathroom door sends adrenaline through my veins
Now I spend my time just waiting…
And waiting
And waiting
And waiting
Waiting…
waiting…
waiting…

wait

I can no longer feel my legs,

I've been waiting too long.

This lady won't leave but I have to get out.

I stand, I walk out, I wash my hands, I freeze.

I can feel her piercing eyes and I hear her inhale, I flinch awaiting her words,

"You know that you're in the ladies' room, right?"

I look up from my hands, into her eyes, and I walk out.

I've chosen a battle that I cannot possibly win.

The next day…

I walk into the room, the sign reads "Men's Room"

Now I feel okay.

On the Rise

by Lyne Odhiambo

Saw you at the park last fall
lounging in your hot air balloon
by the red-orange treetops.
You were apple slices with
simmered down caramel
sauce on the side,
a blissful crunch in your nature,
a fruit harvested in between
the seasonal extremes.
You had me at "they/them,"
Got me dizzy in the clouds
as you showed me how to
rise above binaries.

Along for the Ride

by Lauren Stone

Content warning: description of physical injury

Ollie had not woken up today and planned on being a patient at his own hospital. He almost wanted to laugh at the irony of it all — a doctor lying on a gurney, barely conscious, just like the patients he was so used to seeing and treating.

Sirens rang in his ears as he was loaded up into the ambulance, flashing lights as the legs of the gurney were pushed up into its body and they slid him in. The paramedics he knew so well, Morino and Ramirez, looked down at him, concerned.

"How you feelin', Doc?" Morino, the back-seater, asked as he stood and reached over Ollie to grab a splint on the other side of the rig. Ollie groaned, put his head back. Pain shot through his leg, enough to make his eyelids flutter and clamp his jaw shut.

Morino continued, "You're gonna have a story to tell when we get you back up on your feet, man."

The sirens were still wailing as they pulled up into the ambulance bay. Morino rattled off vitals as he opened the door, and Ramirez pushed him out of the rig. Ollie glanced at the people in the bay and laughed.

"You know what, can I get a different doctor?" he asked jokingly as they set him down. And then he passed out, his vision going black.

"Alright, let's go!" Morino told the small gathering of doctors, beginning to wheel the gurney into the ER and holding a bag valve mask over Ollie's face in an attempt to help him breathe.

The ER was always a chaotic mess, but it was even more so when one of the trauma patients being rushed in was one of their own. Heads turned, the squeaky eraser on the board came to a sudden stop, and the ring of the phones was clearly heard over a quiet bustle.

And then everything suddenly snapped back, the ringing phones were drowned out by the harsh yelling and footsteps on tiled floor. Nurses came in a pack, doctors ran over to quickly glance at the chart, the monitor, and then at the patient — no, at Ollie.

His brow was furrowed, pain clearly evident on his pale face. He looked so small, lying there on the gurney, helpless. His breaths were harsh and forced, catching in his throat, his chest rising and falling in quick succession.

"Prep for intubation," someone walked into the room, gently telling orders, and immediately everything stilled. It was Casey Rhodes, chief of ER, their most experienced attending physician. "I want one R2, one R1, two nurses, and a student. Everyone else, get back out and start taking care of the patients we had before Winogrodzki came in."

Casey Rhodes had a commanding voice, and he used it well. More than half the doctors in the room left, wishing them well.

Rhodes walked over, slipped on his gloves, and reached for the prepped intubation kit. Ollie stilled a few seconds after the sedative and paralytic were given by the nurse, and Rhodes expertly guided the tube down Ollie's throat, clipping on the bag.

"Equal breath sounds bilaterally," Reagan, his second-year resident, told Rhodes, and he nodded.

Rhodes responded, "I paged surgery before he came in, they're holding a room." He peeled off his gloves, tossed them into the wastebasket, stood in the now silent trauma room. Nothing but him and the quiet racing of his heartbeat.

***

Ollie's leg was a mess. A complete, utter disaster of a break, bone shards shining and gleaming under bright surgical lights. The surgeons probed and picked out fragments, made a small incision and spread it to see the full extent of the wound and remove the bullets still in his leg.

Fragments, shards, pieces.

***

Instead of the harsh tone of his alarm clock, Ollie was awoken by his bedroom door opening with a gentle creak. Carter jumped up onto the bed, tail wagging and large paws making indents in the mattress.

"Carter," Ollie groaned, rolling over and opening bleary eyes. "My shift doesn't start until seven."

The great dane's mouth opened wide, tongue lolling, happy expression glued to his face. Carter continued to wag his tail, nosing at Ollie's shoulder as if to say, "Get up; it's time to go!"

Ollie complied, rolling out of bed and sitting on the corner of the mattress, taking a few seconds to search under the bed for his prosthetic. He fished it out and quickly put the stump of his right leg in the sleeve and then the socket, placing a hand on his left knee as he stood. His current prosthetic was nothing fancy, just a temporary fitting. Ollie yawned and stretched, wearily looking over at Carter. Carter was lying on the bed now, giant head on Ollie's pillow, tail thumping gently on the sheets.

Ollie smiled and walked out of his bedroom, heading toward the kitchen. His gait wasn't perfect yet — he still had to work on the way his prosthetic swung out slightly, the motion of his foot. But he was quickly making progress, and he would be getting his permanent prosthetic at the end of the day today, after his shift in the ER.

He peered out his front door and was quickly blinded by the whiteness of his surroundings — it had snowed. Carter came running with an elated bark that reverberated through the house before he plunged into the snow outside, head emerging with tongue lolling once more.

"You're an idiot, Carter," Ollie deadpanned, staring at the massive dog as he leaped around the front yard, diving and running through mounds of white.

***

Ollie made himself a cup of watered-down coffee while opening up his locker and storing his heavy coat and crutch in the doctor's lounge, hand ruffling through hair still wet from a hot shower.

The door to the lounge opened, and Ollie's head turned towards the noise automatically. A smile spread across his face, teeth showing slightly.

"Hi Casey," Ollie murmured, closing his locker and spinning the dial. "Coffee?" he offered, motioning toward the brewing pot letting off wisps of steam.

"Sure, thanks," Casey said with a smile back, his smile a little grin that made a small blush rise to Ollie's cheeks.

A smile shouldn't have been able to make a blush rise to Ollie's face, make his heart flutter in his chest. But even those small actions, little acts of gratitude and friendliness, did this to him. He felt like he was in high school again.

Ollie made his way back over to the coffee pot, pouring two cups. Steam rose, swirling into the air. Ollie offered one of the cups to Casey. Their hands brushed against one another, Ollie's nimble fingertips against Casey's rough palm, and heat rose in Ollie's face once more.

"You're getting your permanent prosthetic today, right?" Casey asked, eyes the color of his coffee gently peering at Ollie. Ollie nodded, looking down.

"Yeah, I am. I have an appointment with my prosthetist after my shift," he said, taking a sip of the scalding hot coffee. It burned the back of his throat.

"I can drive you, if you'd like," Casey offered, and Ollie's eyes flicked up, wide. "I, we, y'know, we get off at the same time today, so I figured …"

Ollie managed to form a sentence, "That would be very nice."

"Sounds good," Casey told him, pushing his glasses up further on the bridge of his nose.

Ollie nodded and looked down at his watch. It was seven now, so he grabbed a pen, scribbled his name on his coffee cup, and began to make his way out the door of the lounge.

A hand on his shoulder stopped him. He turned and it was Casey, hand still on his shoulder.

Spontaneously Ollie leaned forward and his lips gently grazed Casey's cheek. He turned his face and their noses brushed against one another, the frame of Casey's glasses pressing into Ollie's browline. Ollie stepped back with a small, blushing smile and placed his hand on Casey's, which was seemingly paralyzed on Ollie's shoulder.

"We have to work now," Ollie murmured, intertwining their fingers.

"I know," Casey told him, hand gently dropping from Ollie's shoulder, their hands still clasped. "Doesn't mean I don't want to just stay here with you for a while."

"Here?" Ollie asked, lips spreading into a smile. "How about my house, after the appointment? You can say hello to Carter again."

Casey had taken care of Carter while Ollie was still recovering in the ICU, and then helped walk him when Ollie was confined to a wheelchair.

"That would be lovely," Casey said. The both of them were still smiling like fools at each other.

"I really need to go out and run the board now," Ollie told Casey.

"Alright, I know," Casey said, opening the door and ushering Ollie out.

***

"Bethany!" Ollie shouted over the din of the ER, spotting the other third year resident as she came walking in. He had a few cases he needed to hand off to her.

"I know, I know, I'm late — just give me your charts and run. I'll figure them out," she told him, sweeping strands of wild ginger hair out of her face.

"Alright, thank you!" Ollie said with a smile, handing over a stack of charts and records. Bethany groaned, plopping the pile down.

Suddenly Casey appeared at the admit desk, eyes running over the board methodically. He asked Ollie, "Ready to go?"

"I will be in a minute. I just need to go grab my things. I'll be right out," Ollie promised.

The doctor's lounge was quiet as he opened his locker, switching his white coat for his heavy brown jacket. He folded the collar down, buttons just the middle.

Ollie met Casey back at the admit desk, and they slipped out the ambulance bay doors quietly.

"Thanks for driving me," Ollie murmured as the two of them made their way to Casey's car.

"It's really no problem," Casey told him, opening the passenger's side door for Ollie with a smile, then extending his hand.

"Such chivalry," Ollie joked, taking Casey's hand and lowering himself into the seat. The car door closed, and Casey made his way around to the driver's side and started the car. The engine rumbled underneath both of them as they pulled out of the parking garage and into the Chicago night.

***

"This feels amazing," Ollie said as he walked the length of the exam room in his new prosthetic, then sat back down on the bench. He'd be fawning over this leg for a while. It was half cherry wood, half 3D-printed carbon fiber, and hollow inside. The lightness and grain of the wood gently contrasted with the near-black swirls of the carbon fiber, and he loved the feel of it too. No more pins, just compression socks and a suction mechanism.

"It really is state of the art," his prosthetist told him. "I'm glad we could make this happen for you, Olivier."

"And I thank you for it," Ollie said, smiling.

"You know what to do, but call if you have any problems," the prosthetist instructed Ollie. Ollie nodded, then walked out of the room to go find Casey in reception.

"All done," Ollie said with a smile, sitting down next to Casey. The cherry wood gleamed in the soft light.

"It's beautiful," Casey murmured, grasping Ollie's hands. "Just like you."

Ollie blushed, turning his gaze away from Casey's, but then turned his gaze back. Their eyes met, gray-blue against coffee brown, and all of a sudden their noses were touching, Ollie's eyelashes fluttered against Casey's. They both leaned in and their lips met, a soft, gentle kiss. Ollie never wanted it to end.

These Feelings

by Sarah Gahl

The thoughts I have are hidden away and the fear of sharing them is keeping them astray.

There's no one who knows, knows one who can see, no one I trust to tell of my deed.

There is a time of doubt and a time I fear if I show my true colors,

Will they listen?

Will they hear?

Will I be scared to show her and everyone I know, who I really am?

The girl that I want them to see.

These feelings I feel have been hidden for so long, the horrors they hold make me question if I belong.

The emotions that run so deep in my veins have been treated like a virus and killed away.

It comes to a point where the question resides, will those that I love still be by my side.

Will they cherish my feelings and respect my love, or will this disown me and just give up?

These feelings I feel have been hidden for so long that sometimes I forget they actually belong.

These feelings I feel are so unique that they scare me when they make my heart beat.

I think I understand who I was chosen to be but I will never know when it's time to

share the real me.

These feelings I have, have been hidden very deep but with time and patience, I will soon share the missing piece.

I don't know when,

I don't know how,

but it will be soon and I will scream it aloud

I will scream so loud that the whole world will hear, and my name will go down as the girl who let out all the feelings that she kept from reach.
When they finally know I hope they won't change, there is nothing different, just more knowledge they will obtain.
When I finally tell them will they still be the same?
Oh I don't care, I can't even bear to think of the negative outcome when there's so much to gain
I can't wait for the day
I truly can't wait
When I wake up in the morning with a big smile on my face.
When the birds sing and there is a steady breeze, when I can sit outside and just breathe.
No worry
No care
No FEAR
Just happiness, and freedom, and joy all throughout the atmosphere
Oh I can't wait
I truly cannot wait
When they finally know the feelings I hold,
the emotions I bear, and the love I want to share.
I am no fool I know that this dream might not come true, I know that they might turn away and never look at me the same, I know that I may be alone, but there are people that I know will love me,
People that I know will care.
People that will welcome me and hold me and remind me that someone is always there.
So when fear tries to hold me and hide me in my room I push fear back and tell it
I am not alone, unlike you.
Because I have another family, one that is always near, one that I know when I need them
will hold me and wipe my tears.

A family that is big and strong and wise.
A family that has gone through horrors and crimes.
A family that has grown and stood tall.
A family with no fears, like none at all.
A family that is supportive, caring, and sweet.
A family with an open arm,
A family with reach.
A family that is mine
A family that will help me shine.
A family that is full of love and would never just give up, no matter how hard, no matter the time. When I get scared to scream aloud, I remember that
I should have no fear, because no matter how far,
I am never alone because
they will always be there, and
They will forever be my Home
So here I go.

Favorite Flavor of Ice Cream

by T.J.

Do you remember being a little kid on your bestest behavior
And being rewarded with any flavor of ice cream you wanted
After choosing your award to be ice cream
Do you remember how you were having such a hard time choosing between chocolate and vanilla and strawberry
Do you remember how you fell in love with all three
Do you think you could understand if I explained to you I am at once all three flavors of ice cream
Do you think you could fall in love with me the way you fell for all three flavors individually
Could you love me even while I melt inside of myself
No longer would I be solid
Only liquid
Only fluid
Could you love this fluid
Could you be the cone of my ice cream and keep me put
Keep me contained
Could you hold this fluid thing and still find my beauty
I am woman
I am man
I am neither
I am both
I am strawberry
I am chocolate
I am vanilla
I am your favorite ice cream but you no longer want me
You no longer like me
And who is to hold this liquidated ice cream now if not you
If not myself
If I cannot hold myself

Who will hold this fluid thing

Who will make me their favorite flavor of ice cream

Who will love me

Like I am not just runny ice cream

Who will love me even when the love for myself becomes just as runny

Until I run out of love for myself

Tell me

Can I be your favorite flavor of ice cream

Can I be the reward you chose to have

Can I be your reward

When you have been on your bestest behavior

Ira Lee, Always Me

by Nick Susa

Ira paced around her office as the workday ended. Soon all the workers would go home to their families, and she would be free to ponder the choices that the day had presented. As she adjusted her tie, she glanced down at her desk to the framed photo of her parents and her in the creek by her childhood home. She could still hear the slow trickle of the water and the idle noises of the local birds.

So much had changed since that day by the creek. She had moved to the city for one thing, and started a successful business for another. However, looking at her life, nothing had changed more than her relationship with her father. It wasn't bad, just awkward. It wasn't how it was that day on the creek where he taught her how to shoot an arrow or how to blub like a fish. The relationship was quiet, a live and let live sort of matter that Ira never mentioned to her friends or coworkers.

It all began when she was thirteen years old. Her best friend lived across the creek, just far enough from her parents' call. Once or twice a week she would go over there to play dress up or hide and go seek among the far-reaching trees. She always had to go home early though, especially when the two played dress up. Whenever Ira got home, she made little conversation about the actions of the day. Instead, she would focus on helping prepare dinner.

At this moment, Ira pulled away from the photo and began to move around the room. It was too late. Her father's voice already started to ring out from her memory.

"Noah, it is best to prepare the food this way," it said.

It was strange to hear her dead name when her dad wasn't actually around. But that wasn't the biggest problem. It was that on a night like any other, her dad never said that phrase to her.

Ira had returned from her friend's house and was getting ready to cut some vegetables like normal when her friend's mom burst through the door. Then a quiet came over the kitchen as Ira's mother called her dad into the room. They talked for forever. Longer than forever. Ira did her best with the food on her own, but it wasn't as good as when she made it with her family. In a way, she felt selfish, she only made the food so that everyone could talk around the table instead of in hushed whispers.

"I finished making dinner, would you like to join us?" Ira announced, speaking directly to her friend's mother.

It was no use, her friend's mom didn't want to stick around. In fact, she left immediately, before even giving a yes or no answer. But this was just the opportunity that Ira thought she needed to learn about what was so secret just a moment before.

The family sat down and it was within moments that Ira had realized that her parents knew. She had wanted to tell them. She had planned to tell them. She wasn't ready yet. They weren't ready yet. Had her friend sold her out? No, it wasn't possible. At least not probable, they had been doing this for years. Trading clothes, that is. Ira gave him the clothes that belonged to "Noah" for a day and he would give her the clothes she would wear for hours at a time. Maybe the door was silent as his mom had crept in from working around the town. Maybe Ira had forgotten something at his house. Maybe her best friend had run out of time, and his mom caught him changing back into a skirt only to realize the pants he had taken off had Ira's dying name sewn poorly on the inside. The silence hurt more than an attempt at speaking would have.

Halfway through the meal, her father had made a decision. Or rather was in the middle of making it. He opened his mouth and stretched like he was about to make a speech, only he would give up part way and return to the meal. Her mother said nothing, did nothing, every once in a while she would smile a half-smile but that was all. Someone had to say something, and finally, the will or necessity pushed Ira's voice forward.

"So, what was that all about?" she asked.

Her mother started, "It's just that she is concerned about her daughter. She, uh, saw her wearing clothes with your name stitched in them. So she was wondering if—"

Her father had cut her mother off, "Noah, I need the truth. What exactly are you doing at that house? Is it sex? Is it something else? If you lie, I will find out."

He was angry. He was so direct. He wanted an answer, yet it seemed impossible for Ira to find the right words, the right explanation. He was becoming impatient; his face was scrunching up with every wasting second.

"It's not sex," Ira said.

"So it's something else," her mother said. She looked hopeful for a moment that it was really nothing.

Ira's father did not share the sentiment.

"So what is it?" he asked.

"You were sort of already told, but I suppose I should explain. Sometimes when I go over there, we aren't playing around in the trees. Sometimes we never leave the house. You see…" The words were failing. "I don't … and he doesn't…"

Ira's mother stuck out her hand and grasped Ira's. It was clear she had no idea what was going on, but she was there. The hand helped. It wasn't powerful, but it was enough. Still scary, still hard to find the right things to say, but it was okay. At least, that was what the hand was saying to Ira at that moment.

"Dad," there were tears welling up in Ira's eyes, "I'm not your son." A mess of confusion ran around the room as the rest of the sentence broke with Ira's voice. "I'm your daughter."

The hand was closer now, firmer now. Ira knew it would be okay, with her mom it was okay. Her father didn't understand. He got up and started to leave the room. He was almost too far when he stopped at the doorway.

"Noah, we will talk about this at another time. Clean the kitchen," he said, but it was hard to hear. The tears shared between the two women in the kitchen drowned the sound out.

It was the sound of the tears in her memory that brought Ira back to her office. The office where the tears strolled silently down her face once more. So much had happened, after all, she was still here. She looked at the clock, it was past eleven. At her house, her dad would be asleep and she wouldn't have to face him calling her "Noah" today. There was still plenty to think about for her business, but in her nostalgic distraction, it seemed so far away.

Ira sat down in her chair for the first time that night, and as she spun slowly back and forth across her office, she whispered softly to herself, "Ira Lee, always me."

Kiss

by Kendelle G.

Hushed whispers float on the night.
A boy catches them quick.

He holds the words close
before stumbling over his own.
Not as poetic,
not as quiet.

Moonlit laughter floats back in return.

His cheeks darken,
lips purse around
soundless sweet talk.
The sound stolen by
the plush of the other boy's lips.

A boy's eyes flutter.
He feels himself sink
Deep into the depths of the other.

Wanting to drown in pleasure when
Dripping down the throat
Of the lips he craves, a cross
Of silver grips him by his throat
And pulls him tight.

Shame
Kisses his lips.
A boy fights, screams and suffocates
In the God he trusts.

Elijah

by Victor Long

"Eliza! Breakfast is ready!"

Elijah stared in the mirror, looking at his body with a critical eye — any misplaced bulge, any flare of hip, any softness…

"Eliza!"

Elijah jumped, the motion revealing that he was in fact not flat, but he had no time to fix that now. He adjusted his beanie, hair tucked in a haphazard net of bobby pins under it, before grabbing his backpack and running downstairs to his mother. She was tapping her foot impatiently, curls in a chaotic bun on top of her head.

"Eliza, honestly!" His mother shoved a plate of eggs and bacon at him, shouting over the screams of his infant sister, Lizzie. The baby in question had turned her breakfast into a mess of mush across her table.

"If you spent less time hiding your hair, you wouldn't be late so often!" His mother was attempting to clean the mess, and Elijah ducked his head, face flushing with embarrassment.

"If you would just let me cut it—"

"Eliza, enough with the haircut, you have gorgeous hair and it looks fine the way it is," she replied.

This was a conversation they'd had many times before. Elijah asked to get his haircut, his mother shouted, he gave up and bought more bobby pins. Wash, rinse, repeat.

"You really are a pretty girl, sweetheart, you shouldn't hide it all in your silly hats."

Lizzie had finished her food. Elijah's mother quickly freed her from the chair before a temper tantrum could begin.

Elijah sighed, giving up for the morning and tucking into his breakfast. He'd heard that line before, too. He spent the rest of his morning in a fog, until lunch — that's when the beginning of the end came.

"Hey Elijah," Chloe sat beside him at the lunch table, braids bouncing as she practically vibrated beside him. "So, I have an idea."

Oh no, "What?"

"So your hair has been bothering you, right? Well, I have these really good scissors, and we have a whole lunch hour … we can cut it!"

Elijah didn't know what to do. His mother would be furious, but his head was sore every night because of the bobby pins, and it'd be nice not to wear a hat.

"Let's do it."

Elijah had no idea how they didn't get caught. They were in the girls' bathroom, using Chloe's hoodie as a poncho to protect Elijah's clothes, and he was sitting precariously on the counter, body contorted to fit, and his hair falling into the trashcan, bobby pins sitting at the bottom of the bag. Chloe used a water bottle to wet his hair, and he felt the cold weight straightening the curls.

"I even brought a comb!" Chloe exclaimed. Chloe brushed his hair out, and then he heard it.

Snip. Snip. Snip.

"I'm going in chunks, not all at once, in case we don't finish," Chloe warned.

Elijah closed his eyes against the sound. Snip. Snip. Sniiiip. It felt like he was there for an eternity, listening to the sound of his hair falling away. His head felt lighter, and each time Chloe combed it out, his hair fell sooner.

Just as the bell rang, signaling the end of lunch, Chloe squealed happily, and helped Elijah sit up. She snatched up paper towels to dry it some, and Elijah saw himself in the mirror. He began to cry.

There, staring back, was his reflection — with hair sticking out just past his ears. He felt … more himself. He ran a hand through it, his fingers losing contact quickly, and the curls fell back to his ears. He brushed it back, and it followed quickly. He moved his head around, and it barely moved.

"It looks amazing, if I do say so myself," Chloe said, and it snapped Elijah out of his reverie.

Elijah shoved his beanie back on, "Mom's gonna be pissed."

Even so, Elijah smiled for the rest of the afternoon.

The Rhythm of Hallucination

by Kimia Dasteh Goli

Every one of us
Has a story;
In a tragic, intimidating night.
My story
Happened to be tonight.

Shedding tears,
Tightening eyelids,
Panicking.

As the clock hand
Runs away,
Wishing the fear
Goes away.

I don't know
Why I'm blaring
Out of my mind;
So, the world
Can feel my pain?
So, his terrifying presence
Would probably end?

Tick…
Tock…

He's going nowhere.

My temper's
Rising high.

Tick…
Tock…

But he's
Going nowhere.

Imagine me,
Through the times,
His cold, wild wrists
Twisting around mine.

"Leave me alone"
Just
"Leave me alone."

Or the times,
My eyes' bloody victims
Were copiously fainting,
One by one;

Gently
Fading away,
As his gravelly scream
Becomes clearer.

The sun comes up.
The light is so bright.
That, paradoxically, starts a dark flame
Right into my eyes.

Closing my eyes,
Capturing old memories,

And allowing myself to taste the feeling.

It's been seven hours.
I'm shifting in my bed
Knowing that I did not
Get a wink of sleep last night.

Now, I'm standing
Right in front of a mirror,
Looking into 'her' eyes,
And believing, he's not here.

But I wasn't looking at her at all.
Instead, I could see his shadow
Hugging mine,
In the very back of this frame.

So, I threw his shiny memento
At him, across the room.
And the mirror, vividly, reflected nothing,
Other than a broken imagination.

I started laughing.
Or more realistically, crying,
'Cause that was the time
I realized I'd been living
With him, in my mind,
For all these years, forever.

My mind was overwhelmed
With a fear of facing him again,
Who was no longer alive in

Anywhere other than my brain.

I was choked with emotion
And I couldn't help
But to deal with that monster in my head.

'Cause every time
I attempt to showcase my true self,
I break the old me into bloody pieces.

Why is Sexuality Taboo Among African Women?

by Sandrice Grace Bangura

Content warning: sexual assault mention

No matter what age you are, if you have West African parents, you've heard the saying, "Sex before marriage is disgusting," or something like that. It's even in our culture to make sure if a girl is still "pure," a white cloth is placed under her on her wedding night. Why, though?

Even before I had any sexual encounters, I was very vocal about this one point: sexuality is only a tiny fraction of what a person is, believes and stands for. But as I grew up, as soon as someone said, "This posin free oo" (this means in my native language that the person has loose morals), they instantly were branded as a bad person.

That, I'm sure you have the common sense to grasp, isn't true. But the question always crosses my mind, "Why is the topic of sex still so taboo for African women today?" As soon as the topic is brought up, an uncomfortable cough is forced and the subject is changed or pushed into a sermon of how and why that is disgusting conduct. If it's so disgusting, then why is that the process in which procreation takes place (for heterosexual couples) and an expression of love? If it's so sinful, then why not educate us on why and bring up better points than that one point raised in a patriarchal society all the time: "It's your husband's right to meet you a virgin."

Last I checked, another person does not control my body, nor do the expectations my parents set for me. I own my body and if I want to give it to someone who cares about me, my sexuality will be freely expressed. Even though I have the privilege of consent, lots of women don't.

This may be hard to imagine, but bear with me for a minute. Imagine being raped and having your innocence stolen from you at a tender age. So, to hide the shame this might cause, you sweep it under the rug. And you meet a person whom you decide you want to spend the rest of your life with so you tell them your experience, hoping that it will draw you closer, but because you are no longer "pure" by traditional circumstances, they leave. That would be sad, wouldn't it? You were being judged off of not who you are or what you stand for, but by your sexual past or present (not something you chose at all for yourself), something that doesn't even make up a solid 10 percent of who you are.

Can we please stop stigmatizing premarital sex and just sexuality in general? Instead of telling a girl that she shouldn't even talk about those things, create open discourse to educate them of what all of it really entails, their choices and how they can act wisely and keep themselves safe.

If they want to wait for marriage, big ups to them. But sex isn't the enemy for young African women and girls today. The indoctrinated stigma (that it's always been a man and a woman and how a woman needs to learn her place) is the perpetrator and we can choose to fight it or allow time to pass us by another 500 years before we realize that being able to love who you want to love how you want to love them is a form of empowerment.

I Am Not Your Boyfriend

by Jaxson Butler

I am not your boyfriend.
I am not blonde.
I am not short.
My voice isn't high pitched.
I am not your boyfriend.
No, I don't have a boyfriend, and I don't need to.
I don't walk around looking like I only come out when the rain goes away,
But I only come out when the rain goes away.
I am not your boyfriend.
Yes I watch sports, in fact you could say I watch people play with balls a lot.
I'm not ashamed of anything, in fact I'm quite proud.
It's just that when your "gaydar" can't detect me, to you, I become my own worst enemy.
I am not your boyfriend.
I am not your yaoi fantasy.
I am not your archery practice, and even if you shoot me 49 times,
I will still have a *pulse.*
I am *not* your boyfriend.
I am *not* your gay best friend.
I am *not* a token in your collection of coins.
I am myself.

Pink Rhinestones

by Avalon Mist Bruno

I fell in love with you at your sixteenth birthday party
I was the only one there from our high school
The only white person in the barn belonging to your tío
I was worried what your family would think of me
But your mamá and abuelita both hugged me as if I was family
And it kept my anxiety at bay.
When you walked in
I was stunned.
You were already gorgeous, but you looked otherworldly in pink satin
The pink rhinestones all over your dress shimmered under the lights
Almost as bright as your surprised smile.
Everyone else at the party were old friends and family
And I watched you hug your parents
Imagining those arms around me.

I stood with some girls my age
Your old friends from Chicago
Who were surely more important to you than I was
But when you walked over
Strutting in your heels
Commanding respect and taller than me for the first time ever
You caught my eye and your smile grew.
I was the first friend you hugged.

I fell deeper in love with you when we saw the school musical together.
Shoulder to shoulder, I was concentrating more on how you smelled
Than to the students on the stage.
I'd sat next to you in class before
But I'd never felt your gentle heat for so long.
I decided before you arrived that I would tell you how I felt

And face whatever consequences came from it
But you saw another friend and we sat with her.
While I was still happy to be in your presence
And while I knew it would be a rude and awful thing to do
I wanted nothing more than to pull you into a corner during the intermission
Throw all caution to the wind
And kiss you.

I wanted to feel your lips on mine
That's all I wanted I needed it just something anything
Please.

Your scent soaked into the side of my shirt
Trailing from my sleeve down to my hip
When I got home I sat on my bed and breathed you in until there was no trace left
Your scent intoxicated me with visions of a life I knew I couldn't have
I wanted it so much god I wanted it.
I couldn't place the scent and I still can't
A mixture of soaps and spices and something heady
But I know that it made me feel at home.
It made me feel safe and grounded
I knew more than ever that I wanted to be with you forever.

At that point I didn't care if it was platonic or romantic
I just needed you so much too much
You were an addiction for me and I always needed more
And even after more than a year when I thought my feelings would calm down
That the raging hormones would have abated
They seemed to grow stronger every day until it seemed that
Aside from homework

All I thought about was you.

It was a Tuesday in May of sophomore year
I asked you to meet me after school
I told you that I had a "tiny crush" because the truth was too much.
I don't think I'll ever be able to look you in the eyes
And tell you that for a year and a half
I envisioned growing old with you
The first and only person I've ever truly been in love with.

When I told you
You sighed
And my heart broke.

We're still friends, right?
Of course, you told me.
I could hear pity in your voice.

The worst part was seeing you the next day
Having to sit next to you in class and pretend like nothing happened
We watched a movie in class
I was so glad that the lights were turned off because I was crying.
I didn't want you to see my tears.

It's been almost three years since that day and I can safely say that I'm alright.
No classes together in junior year helped me keep my distance.
My friends helped me mend my heart.
I haven't felt anything that even compares to what I felt towards you
But it's okay because I have the rest of my life to find someone who will love me back.

But still

We had a class together senior year
And you were so nice to me all the time and sometimes it was too much
Because even when I told myself that I was over you
You smiled at me or you laughed
And my heart ached.
I know that I'll never forget you.
I'll never forget your scent or your passion or how we clicked like puzzle pieces.

I never told you this
But two pink rhinestones fell off your dress
On the night of your sixteenth birthday party
And I picked them up off of the floor and tucked them away into my purse.
I put them next to the origami gum wrapper cranes you made for me
And that day in May when my eyes were blurry with tears
I put all of your gifts away in a jewelry box drawer.

Sometimes I open that drawer and I think of you.
The way the rhinestones reflect the light reminds me of your eyes
Even though they don't shine as bright or as warm.

Bisexual

by Kailea

I am bisexual
In my heart,
I can only speak in whispers
I'll never feel like
I belong
I know that
I'm too gay for society and too straight for the community
It's stupid to think that
I will be accepted
Anywhere

Anywhere
I will be accepted
It's stupid to think that
I'm too gay for society and too straight for the community
I know that
I belong
I'll never feel like
I can only speak in whispers
In my heart,
I am bisexual.

I Can't Do This Anymore

by M.F.

Overeager and sensitive
Love bubbles to the surface
And lingers, caught in the fiber of your being.
Falling is terrifying,
Creating a pit in your stomach,
The uncertainty of the ground looming below
An ever-present horror.
I've fallen three times.
Every time was terrifying, exhilarating.
The first time, I felt like I was on fire.
She kissed me at a football game
And I felt like a cliché, like a movie character.
I'd never seen something like that in a movie.
I cried for an hour after.
Despite it all, I fell fast.
I counted the days, the months.
And then, right before eleven months of falling,
Everything was wiped away with five words.
"I can't do this anymore."
Love is a goddamn atrocious thing, I thought.
She never cared as much as I did.
For her, I was a blip
For me, it was everything.
The second time I fell, it came with desperate and shaking breathe.
I stared at my ceiling every night,
Knowing that I shouldn't love her.
She's my best friend, I thought, I can't do this.
"Bibimbap," she said, pushing the bowl across to me
I whispered the word to myself, over and over
It sounded light, airy, foreign.

Her smile made me fall.
That pit in my stomach returned, and terror followed.
I kissed her in her bedroom,
Listening to Taylor Swift and dancing.
I cried again, feeling guilty and perverted.
She kissed the top of my head,
And told me that we can't help who we love.
I wished, I prayed that I could help who I loved.
She told me in a quiet voice, weeks later,
"I'm sorry. I can't do this anymore."
She said the timing was wrong,
That she wishes she could love me the way I deserve.
I felt numb.
Love catches on you like Velcro,
But eventually you have to tear Velcro off.
The third time feels different.
Freer, maybe,
Like the Velcro hasn't caught yet.
I'm terrified that those words will come a third time,
That I will crash into the ground again,
Left feeling numb and broken.
The guilt still comes occasionally,
But I was able to kiss her without crying.
My love isn't wrong, isn't worthy of guilt.
Love, though, despite who it's with,
Is a goddamn atrocious thing.
God doesn't have anything to do with it, though.
God doesn't care, can't care.
They just watch, unfazed, as we fall.
They watch as we hit the ground,
As we stay falling for decades, if we're lucky.
They watch, and they observe.

I don't know yet if the fall is worth it.
Maybe that terror has a place, has a meaning.
I would like to know what that meaning is.
Can I do this anymore?

To Be a Princess

by Aliyah W. Berg

As a little girl, I was never told that gay meant bad. I was told that every princess needs a prince and I was told that of course one day I would want children. I was told I didn't understand the ways of adults and that I should sit and listen. I found myself having crushes on boys because that's what everyone else did. My best friend liked a boy with glasses, so I decided to like a boy with red hair. I was asked out by a boy in a sweater and I accepted because the girl next to me took a purple marker and circled yes for me.

In fourth grade, there was a girl that I always wanted to be around. She sat in the desk next to me, a book always in hand. I figured she was my best friend, except I wanted to be with her always even when she told me to play a different game on the monkey bars. I always complied. I watched as she ran across the field with such speed in her glittery, pink shoes and I watched in wonder. I wanted to run that fast with her. She loved horses and books about butterflies, so I began to love those too. She introduced me to Studio Ghibli films and we spent hours pretending to be the characters. It wasn't until later when I realized I didn't just "like" her, I "like-liked" her. Somehow I knew that that thought wasn't allowed. I couldn't like-like her because girls are supposed to like boys. Princesses to princes, but to myself, I thought, "If boys have cooties why should I like them?"

In seventh grade, there was another girl dressed in black with short brown hair. She was the loudest alto in choir class and yet I still wanted her to be louder. We became friends and I decided to ask her out after going to the movies. I remember bursting through the doors exclaiming that she was my girlfriend, her hand in mine, but one of the other girls in my group asked if I was suddenly gay. I said no, because the way she said it made me feel like I needed to take a shower. I dated the girl with brown hair for two weeks before breaking up because I had her over at my house and the entire time, I was terrified she'd let it slip to my mom that we were dating.

In eighth grade, I dated that boy in a sweater and I remember telling him that I thought I was bi and that I didn't want to wear girly clothes anymore. He said that no, I was straight because I was dating him. He said I couldn't wear longer shorts to his house because it wasn't "cute," so I wore pants that whole summer. It wasn't that I didn't feel like a girl — I just didn't want to be seen as a Barbie doll. I wanted to be seen as the girl that loves *Harry Potter* and always helps her friends with their homework. I cut my hair and the boy in the sweater said it was ugly. We dated for a long time; I didn't know how to fight back.

In ninth grade, there was a girl in my English class that had golden hair and green eyes. She said she loved my artwork and wanted to go to a different school. Our conversations were about the books we'd read, how we didn't like gym, and how we didn't get enough sleep. These little spoken words were my only solace in a time where I didn't speak much. I knew she didn't, or couldn't, like girls, so I never said anything. After all, I couldn't like girls either. I occupied my time by convincing myself I had a crush on this wrestling boy when I just wanted to get ice cream with the girl in my English class. That year, the AC broke in our school and she said to me that she looked gross because she'd be sweating. All I remember thinking is how she could never look gross because she rivaled Aphrodite in my mind. But I just replied "same."

In eleventh grade, I liked the same girl, but I couldn't say anything because her father would disown her if he ever found out. She would be hit with a Bible on her way out of the house. I couldn't date her because if I accidentally let it slip, her world would come crashing down around her. I had found out she liked me back in ninth grade but never said anything. For that, I am glad because I wanted her to be safe and happy even if it meant my crush never got pronounced. Being her friend was enough. We are close friends but sometimes it feels like the world is moving slowly around her. She is beautiful but she doesn't seem to see herself in the same light. I think she is most beautiful when she laughs and her green eyes become a little lighter.

Now, I don't know whether or not I can tell my family of my feelings, yet my sister supports me 100 percent. I have talked to some of my friends about liking both girls and boys and how it can be confusing. My friend agrees because she is also bi. We laugh together and show each other cute people on Tik-Tok. My other friend says not to worry because college is coming soon, he's told his mom he's gay but could never tell his dad. The girl with golden hair talks to me about all the boys on her Snapchat and how they're annoying; I just laugh.

I am proud to be who I am and I am proud to have these friends. I may have worn a dress to Sophomore Prom, but I also wore a suit to Junior Formal. I no longer pick and choose who I supposedly like, but instead just figure it out along the way. I treasure my friends and teachers and family that support me and I love supporting them too. I have plans to go to pride this year with my friends and I have had my outfit picked out for two months. I plan to be decked out in rainbows, hand and hand with my chosen family. I heard that princesses need princes, but I am my own leader and I've discovered over time that this world is not a monarchy.

Closets Are for Clothes

by Jeniel Zimmerman

Content warning: hate crime mention

Closets are for clothes,
Not queer people.
Closets are for corduroy jackets and chiffon skirts
Not for hiding away people that make society feel "uncomfortable" —
After all, it's prejudice that built the closets first.

Closets that manifest in the form of teachers' silence,
In the ignorance passed to each generation,
In the constant erasure of queer existence
Until the letters LGBT
Are more like a prison
Than a person's identity.

But I will not let you be invisible anymore.

To the girl crying at the mirror, wishing her body matched the way she felt inside,
I see you.
To the boy so embarrassed by his sexuality that he would have rather died,
I see you.
To the daughter forced to therapy as if homosexuality was something you could get rid of,
I see you.
To the son whose family made religion about hate instead of love,
I see you.
To all the kids hiding in closets,
I see you.

I feel your fear because it is my own:
Of uncertain futures and rocky pasts,
Of guilt and denial and feeling alone;

Of the terrified tears when the man with the gun
Could hate someone like me so much
He'd kill forty-nine people in that gay club;

Of the "no mom, I'm not gay" —
I never wanted to lie to you, mom,
It's just that I was afraid.

But we have nothing to hide;
We do not have to prove our love.
We do not have to prove our love.
I do not have to prove my love.

So I'll shout it out until everybody knows:
I'm here, I'm queer,
And closets are for clothes.

Lost in Denial

by Beatriz Canuto

Boys like girls, girls like boys
That's the way it should be
Or so they said
It's time to be awake

Don't know when it all started
Is this just a trap?
My mind is playing games
Don't see a starting point
No destination on this map

Colors in a black and white world
There's confusion
It's an illusion
How could this be real?
I'm lost in denial

Starting to like her more than him
I don't recall it being this way
Swinging both ways, feeling dizzy
Don't know what to say or choose
As my feelings start to change
I know, life will never be the same

I'm uncovering my true self
Or is my mind just fooling me?
Images of memories turning into blurs
Lies can make you blind
Yet a part of me believes

Colors in a black and white world
There's confusion
It's an illusion
This can't be real
I'm lost in denial

I'm too confused
Too scared
To like someone else
To say it out loud
People will judge
They won't understand

Colors in a black and white world
There's resolution
Not an illusion
This is real

The Wild Girl

by Abigail Lowry

When I was ten, I fell in love for the first time.
She had fiery red hair that matched her fiery attitude. She was brash and bold and reckless.
And I loved her for it.

Because of her I knew what love felt like. Because of her I knew what I felt two years later when I met her.

She had hair like sunshine and eyes like the sky and she could always make me laugh. She asked for help in English class and she would let me talk about my favorite books for as long as I wanted.
And I loved her for it.

She told me pick-up lines that made me weak in my knees and I knew that she meant them so when we were walking home, I kissed her on the cheek and told her how beautiful she was.

And she said:
"I don't feel that way.
I couldn't fall for another girl."
And then she stopped telling me jokes and she didn't ask for my help anymore.

But when I saw her, she always looked like she missed me, and I would wonder if she ever did love me. Just in a different way from how I loved her. And it hurt because I thought I had pushed her away.

A year and a half later I fell in love with her. She had a voice of an angel and a laugh like silver bells. She was shy and quiet, but she would sing her heart out for me.
And I loved her for it.

We'd play duets, her and I, with her on the violin and me on the piano. Some days she would play love songs and I knew they were for me so one day I handed her some flowers and told her how beautiful she was.

And she said:
"I don't feel that way.
I couldn't fall for another girl."
And then she stopped singing to me and she didn't play songs with me anymore.

But when I saw her she always looked like she missed me, and I would wonder if she ever did love me. Just in a different way from how I loved her.
And it hurt because I thought I had pushed her away.

So I decided that I wouldn't fall in love with girls anymore because it only made me hurt, and I kept that promise for three years. I kept it until I saw her.

She was a wild girl with hair as dark as night and stormy gray eyes.
She was wayward and she was chaotic and unruly and defiant and—
But I didn't love her for it.

She would tell me pick-up lines but they were cheesy and they made me snicker instead of swoon and when I laughed she would too and her laugh sounded like the rumble of thunder and—
But I wouldn't love her for it.

She would read any book I talked about so that she could impress me and she sang any love song she heard and she would dance with me and—
But I couldn't love her for it.

Because I knew she didn't mean her pick-up lines and her love songs weren't for me. She was just like every other girl.
Until she wasn't.

She came to me one day with a wild look on her face and she tucked a flower behind my ear and she kissed me and told me how beautiful I was.
And how she loved me.

And I said:
"I feel the same way.
I've fallen for you
Over and over again."
Because she was everything I had ever wanted.

And I loved her for it.

All the Best Love Stories Start with Snow

by Ember Cuddy

The snow blankets the world, quieting our footsteps as we walk, the soft crooning of a singer echoing from the neon lit doorway of the Rialto. The wind trails its cold fingers through my hair and steals my voice as I open my mouth to speak. She looks towards me, questioningly, my words melting away like powdered sugar. The wind whispers to me, returning the phrase to my mouth and caressing the rose on my cheek.

"What did you think of the music?" I ask timidly, shoving my hands further into my pockets and nestling into my scarf.

"It reminds me of the stuff my roommate listens to," she responds with a smile, pushing a long strand of hair behind her ear, before quickly dipping her hand back into the safety of her jacket.

I pull my face from my scarf again, "Yeah?"

"Mhmm. Her music taste is great. She listens to a lot of jazz. She really likes Ella Fitzgerald."

"Ella Fitzgerald? I don't know if I've heard any of her songs."

"You probably have somewhere and just didn't realize. She was a jazz singer back in the 1930s and 50s."

"She sounds awesome."

"Yeah, she was. She had a gorgeous voice," she says, her voice trailing off.

We walk along quietly, the wind hushing us into soft silence. The streetlamps glint on the icy road up ahead. We turn left, passing storefronts closed for the night, signs warning of alarm systems watching us from each window. The snow falls through the air in thick clouds of silver, sticking in her hair and eyelashes. She is so beautiful, all wrapped up in winter, flowers blooming on her cheeks, freckles sprinkled across her skin like stars.

She goes to cross the street, "I parked in the bank parking lot. Where'd you park?"

"I walked from my house," I say.

I look down the street towards the bank. The sign glows orange, the snow interrupting its display. She turns to look and glimpses the temperature just before the sign changes.

"Why? It's two fricking degrees out here! You can't possibly be thinking of walking home," she chided, flinging her hand out of her pocket to gesture at the sign.

"To be fair, it was warmer out here earlier and I only live a few blocks away."

"I don't care if it was warmer out earlier. It is freezing out here! I'll drive you home," she offers, putting up a hand to stop me from saying anything.

I somewhat halfheartedly protest, "You really don't have to."

"Yes, I do. You are not walking out here, alone and in the cold, E. I won't have it."

"Are you sure?"

"Yes."

I duck my head and rub my hands together, trying to warm the tips of my fingers and expel the nervous tension that's been building in me all night. "Alright. Thank you so much."

"You're welcome," she responds, grabbing ahold of my hand and pulling me across the street and towards her car. "Now let's get going. It is freezing out here!"

We slip down the sidewalk, empty buildings towering above us, workers having long since gone home. The darkened windows stare at us like unblinking eyes, watching every move we make. She grips my hand a little tighter. I squeeze her hand, a reassurance that I'm there. She looks at me and smiles. Her smile makes her eyes glisten, softening from amber to the pale green of Spanish moss. The streetlight above us flickers as we reach her car. It's a simple, white Subaru, the outside covered with muddy watermarks. It is just what you'd imagine a lively gay English major to drive.

She pulls out a key and jiggles it into the keyhole of the passenger door. A single click later she swings the door open and gestures to the car.

Tripping over my coat I climb in and pull the cold plastic seat belt over my chest. She pulls open the other door and slides into the car, the wind pushing snow through with her. The car rumbles to life and cold air blows towards me, small snowflakes coming with it.

"I'm so sorry!" she cries, lunging over me to close the vent. "It takes a minute to warm up. I'll drive you home as soon as the windows have cleared up."

Her cheeks, still flushed from the cold, redden just slightly as she pulls her upper body out of my lap and back into her seat. I giggle a little at the look on her face.

"So was date three a success?" I ask her nervously.

"I think so. What do you think? Do we get a fourth date?" she questions, turning towards me to look in my eyes.

"I would like that a lot," I smile, my mouth twitching up at the corners, the nerves in my stomach loosening.

She beams at me causing me to smile wider. "I would too, but for now I suppose I have to take you home. The windows are cleared up."

"Thank you for the best Saturday night I've had in a long while," I whisper.

***

"I brought coffee!" I call to her as she leaves the science building on Tuesday.

She brushes back her bangs and looks around for me. I raise a coffee cup in greeting. She smiles and waves, meandering towards me.

"Hi! How was class?" I ask.

"It was fine. Just the usual. How was work? And what did you get me?" she questions eagerly as I hand her the drink. "Yes! Eggnog latte!" she says as she takes a sip and cheers at the results.

"Work was good," I say as I awkwardly give her a one-armed hug. "I thought I'd treat you since you told me you love eggnog lattes. Plus, it's cold out today and we are not going on the warmest of dates."

"We are not staying outside, are we?"

"Yes, we are, but it'll be worth it! I promise."

We walk to the curb where her car is parked. "You'll have to give me directions so I know where to go."

"You got it. Sometimes I forget you didn't grow up here," I say, sipping from my drink.

"Well, sometimes I forget you did grow up here so I think we're even."

She pulls away from the curb and down the street.

I explain the date as she drives, "So we are going to go and walk around the mansion district. Left. I thought it'd be fun. There are so many … keep going straight … beautiful old houses up there. The amount of quality architecture in this section of town is really quite impressive. There are these big stone houses and some really gorgeous Tudor style mansions. A couple of them have these massive yards and a whole bunch of them have separate guest rooms across the lawn from the main house and stuff. Just wait! You're going to love it. Now I would turn right here and park there and we're good!" I point to an empty spot near the corner of a big stone house.

"This sounds like a lot of fun," she says, sweeping her hair out of her eyes and shifting the car into park.

She comes and opens my door, offering a hand to help me out of the car. I link my fingers with hers and pull her towards me. Hand in hand, I lead her up a hill towards a sprawling Tudor house. It's all straight lines, towering up towards the grey sky, practically reaching for the snowflakes as they find their way to the eaves. The sky is slipping into night and with the snowflakes drifting ever downward it is like every star in the sky decided to fly down, to our town, to see what falling in love looks like.

She is watching the building, smiling up at the Christmas lights decorating every inch of the roof. I'm looking at her and I am thinking about how waltzing is like falling in love. There are three beats in each measure of a waltz. One beat for her, one for me, and one for us. She laughs and it sounds like magic. I can already imagine the things we will do. But I know when we waltz together the first few steps will be hesitant, and we'll get used to the way we move together. We will trip a few times as all new dancers do but we'll laugh, and we'll smile and keep moving.

She turns towards me, cups both sides of my face with her hands and pulls me towards her in a kiss. I can just barely hear a waltz on the wind as I circle my arms around her waist and pull her closer. We sway together and I know two things. We are going to learn to love together and all of the best love stories start with snow.

Road for Two

by Anonymous

As I travel down the street
I wonder what people may think of me
Who will I greet?
Or will all I see
Be dark eyes, judging
Or will they be orbs of light
Perhaps they will be grudging
Because I will demand the right
To be seen as who I am
Happy and gay (though they may seem the same)
And all I will say:
The road is big enough for two
So what do you say we go 'round
Talk for a few
And recognize the sound
Of love

Nuestro Culture Trae Happiness

by Jennifer Almanza

Culture can be defined as the customs, arts, social institutions, and achievements of a group of people.
Hispanic culture is colorful, diverse, and supple.
But, there's this ever increasing disgust for those who aren't normal.
Too dark, too big, too feminine or masculine.
¿Porque me saliste asi? Van a decir que no te crié bien.

I grew up in a traditional household with strict morals
No sex before marriage, wait for true love, marry a good man, education first
Clothes defines you and you need to have a proper definition
Too colorful, too small, too chola or fresa
¿Porque estas vestida como hombre? Van a pensar que eres lesbiana.

The confusion I felt when my close girl friend seemed attractive
It can't be. I won't be. I will only look at males
Being straight is the way to go. Liking both isn't an option
Too crazy, too weird, too different or abhorrent.
¿Porque piensas que te gustan las mujeres? Van a decir que nacistes mal.

I accepted that this was me
But, I'm left alone with wider options.
If you like both girls and boys, why are you single?
Too me, too unique, too ugly yet free
¿Porque no tienes novio? Van a pensar que tienes la personalidad fea.

I am defined by nothing
Sexuality is merely deciding what I love regarding what a person is
Normal is boring and that is not me
Too amazing, too fun, too loving and trusting
¿Porque estas actuando extraña? Van a decir que estas enamorado.

I'm in love with the colors of this culture.

A rainbow of people who even now aren't contained to their flag.

I love both, they love one, we love all

Too united, too carefree, too flamboyant and proud

Al menos, estas feliz.

Burning Butches

by Allo Kerstein

A coalition of ex teenage runaways forge papers and cross borders
speaking and scheming in tongues unintelligible to the city while
squatting in its hollow corpse of our history. At the West Village
Encampment we dedicate art to the dead and say their names:
Hattie and Brian burned in Salem, so we march on Washington,
twenty thousand of us, all in love with one another,

take fire and make it our own, kerosene clad throats and scarlet lips
swallow flames on Lafayette Square. An army of lovers cannot lose
When it is us who invented love, desire, and lust. We take the streets,
staring down the barrel of firing squads while the world ends around us,
just to be together. Our love is libation, revivification, an act of resistance;
And every time we love, we win.

First Love

by Eliana Lazzara

2019 Scholarship Winner

one time I saw love
diagonal from me in the middle school gym,
all brown hair that reflected light like caramel in a glass bowl,
the kind on your grandmother's coffee table
all rosy cheeks and metal mouth
all worn-out converse and black zip-up that advertises a show
none of us watched but pretended to enjoy
because at love's house, everything was enjoyable
I had always been a dog person
but bent over backward trying to like cats
because if love was a cat person
then damnit so was I
love wore t-shirts that were too big
and shorts that had far too many pockets
love had shoulder length hair but always kept it up
love came, and love left
love watched me collapse and build myself back together
love was not at all what I expected
not the prince charming I dreamed of as a little girl
no. there was no knight in shining armor, no trusty steed
to carry us off into the sunset that we couldn't see
love turned out to be the girl in my eighth-grade creative writing class
the one who never wore her hair down
and doodled more than she took notes
and was afraid of dogs
and did not love me back.
love arrived.
love did not stay.

so when love looked different,
all blue eyes and broad shoulders
and a violin hickey from practicing Paganini too much
I did not expect him to stay.
love left just as love had before.
but when love first showed up at my door
and held my hand
and did not mind my worn-out converse
or my shoulder length brown hair
when love did not mind that I had
bent over backward
to be someone love could return to
I was finally able to say
"I feel as though I've seen you
before."

Queer

by Sommer K

Queer. Is that what it's called when you're not able to come out to tell your parents who you are? Queer. Is that what it's called when it feels like your locked away from your own identity?
Queer. Is that what it's called when you're not accepted by your parents?
Queer. Is that what it's called when you're struggling with gender identity?
Queer. Is that what it's called when you can't be you?
Queer. Is that what it's called when you get called strange?
Queer. Is that what it's called when you're put into two categories as a minority?
Queer. Is that what it's called when you're shut out from the world?

Queer. Is a term for gender minorities who are not heterosexual or are not cisgender.
Queer is not what defines you but who you are on the inside,
Queer causes difficulties that some people won't accept, and just because they don't accept you doesn't mean you have to stop being you.
Queer is what I am!
I am a bisexual African American and proud!

I Will Not Stand

by Walter McNaughton

I will not stand for your bigotry
I will not stand for your off-hand comments
I will not stand for your excuses of religion
I will not stand for your broken reasoning
I will not stand for the way that you kill us
I will not stand for the murder of my sisters
I will not stand for the abuse of my brothers
I will not stand for the neglect of my siblings

I will not stand for how history has forgotten us
I will not stand for how I have to yell twice as loud to be heard
I will not stand for how we cannot find bathrooms
I will not stand for how many of us are kicked out
I will not stand for how so many of us are depressed
I will not stand for how many of us can't find safe healthcare
I will not stand for how we have to think about who is safe
I will not stand for how we barely have rights

I will not stand for how many of our youth are on the streets
I will not stand for how many of our youth are bullied or abused
I will not stand for how many of our youth are unable to finish education
I will not stand for how many of our youth are unable to fight back
I will not stand for how many of our youth have no one to talk to
I will not stand for how many of our youth are afraid to ask for help
I will not stand for how many of our youth have harmed themselves
I will not stand for how many of our youth have tried to kill themselves

We are not a choice
We are not a phase
We will not stand down

We will not take your abuse

We will fight back
We will stay strong
We are valid in our gender
We are enough

The Personal as Political

by Dyllan Larmond

June 26, 2015

We sat at the dinner table and CNN was on in the background. It was a hot Sunday evening and the sun slowly wandered behind the trees to signal the end of another day. I remember being happy that night. The Supreme Court had legalized same-sex marriage in all 50 states. I didn't understand then, but deep down it made sense to me.

"I'm happy for them."

First, I was met with silence, then a brief talk on religion and morality. How could something so personal be determined by the government? Why are people who simply want to love being ridiculed and pestered by religious texts written thousands of years ago?

June 2016

I remember the night it all made sense. I was so scared and confused. I cried for hours. Random moments from my childhood resurfaced. How could I have been so blind? I'd been placed in a box — restricted, censored, "protected," and left in the dark about something I'd come to fear about myself. I've heard the low murmurs in the hallways at school, I've been disciplined for being "different," but never told why. "Weird" was what they'd call me. I never got an explanation, only uncomfortable silence knowing that weird was a word for something else. Everything I ever thought I knew about myself was a lie. I represented the word that was never allowed to escape my lips as a child. *Gay.* The word that was hidden from me and scrubbed clean from my vocabulary. It wasn't allowed to exist in my world and here it was, a new part of my identity I did not want to accept. I was a sinner.

January 20, 2017

She told me no. It was pitch black that night and the only sounds that could be heard were my heavy breathing and my feet shuffling against the cold, grey concrete of our garage. We would talk about it tomorrow, but tomorrow never came. All that time spent hiding comfortably in the closet shattered by a rash decision. It felt like I was dying. I was shaking, more nauseous than I had ever felt. The tears in my eyes never threatened to fall. They clung to the inside of my head like the words I wish came out of my mouth that night. They still haven't and for that I'm ashamed.

October 10, 2017

Inadvertently forced underneath everything I'd ever been taught, my emotions and identity were left unattended and cast aside for the sake of everyday things like assignments and social circles. I convinced myself that everything was as it should've been. I had no reason to be unhappy and everything in my life was fine. That was the lie I told myself every day for years.

For the first time in a long time, I let my emotions take over and I sunk to the ground and cried. This was the night my life fell apart and I had no idea why. I finally snapped. I couldn't pick myself up or dust myself off. Everything left unsaid came out and it wouldn't stop. I never thought I'd end up that way.

I asked her to come upstairs. She opened the door and found me sitting in the corner, making myself as small as I could. She asked so many questions, but I didn't have the answers. She hugged me and then she left. I can't remember much else from that night. The weeks and months that followed dragged on in darkness. I was getting worse. It got to a point where the only things I enjoyed were the hours I spent in the darkroom developing photographs from my film camera and finally, at the end of each day where I laid my head on the pillow and went to sleep. Sleep is the way I coped with the mess my life had become. It was the only time I had where I could detach from reality and leave all the pain behind. I spent hours in bed, numbing the pain with dreams and bracing for the moment I had to wake up. Sleep consumed me almost as much as the depression. I lived for the clean, white comforter that absorbed my tears, the purple fleece blanket that carried me away from my struggles, and the blue and gray pillows that cradled my head.

***

I was always restricted but never questioned why. Isn't that just the way things are supposed to be?

I had my first taste of freedom when I came out. It started slowly, but soon enough, I was unstoppable. My goal was to reclaim the pieces of myself that had been taken away, hidden, and destroyed by all the time I spent in silence, hidden away from how wonderful life could be. I wanted to see and be seen, to experience and learn as much as I could. I was voracious to learn my history and spread it to anyone who would listen. The struggle of those who came before me inspires me to keep their fight for liberation alive. It's what keeps me going when I have nothing left to give. It fuels me on the days where all I can manage is to readjust myself in bed every few hours and forget the rest of the world exists.

On the night of June 28, 1969, tensions between the NYPD and the patrons of the Stonewall Inn, a popular gay bar and community space for the LGBTQ community, came to a boiling point. This event led to rioting and the very beginning of the fight for gay rights in America. On the long and difficult road to equality, the community faced oppression from both the American government and society at large that lead to the creation of unjust policies and harassment from all sides, all the while fighting the stigma that came along with the deadly HIV and AIDS crisis of the 80s and 90s.

Individuals such as Harvey Milk, Marsha P. Johnson, and Sylvia Rivera were pioneers of the gay rights movement and spent their lives advocating for equal rights. They dared to live authentically and devoted all of their time and energy to make life better for not only themselves but millions of Americans who faced oppression from both the government and society.

"If a bullet should enter my brain, let that bullet destroy every closet door." This quote comes from Harvey Milk's recordings in the event that he was assassinated. At the height of his political career, Milk emphasized the visibility of gay people to help stop the violence and discrimination that faced the LGBTQ community. Hearing Harvey Milk's last words pushes me every day to live proudly and to never return to the closet. Sharing my truth with anyone who encounters me is a privilege that seemed like an impossible feat only 50 years ago.

During my sophomore year, I began to explore the realm of gay history. After discovering the Stonewall Riots and the brave leaders of the gay rights movement, I knew I was a part of something bigger than myself and had to learn as much as I could. Erasure of my community's history is one of my greatest fears and because so much of my history had been hidden from me, I have readily reclaimed it and will tell anyone who listens.

Soon after this reclamation came the pain. How easy life would be if it was just black and white, true or false, right or wrong. When talking, or even thinking about sexuality, I find it impossible to separate from other parts of my identity. I can't talk about my queerness without including my gender, race, and life experiences that have shaped me into who I am today. The endless intersections, the need to question everything, and the gray areas make my head spin. I truly understand the saying "ignorance is bliss." Some days, I would give anything to be as carefree and mindless as those who would torment me with reckless abandon, all without giving it a second thought. I could live a simple and straightforward life and never be confused again. I could finally categorize and begin to understand the noise and clutter that has become my life, but I understand that living that way would be so dangerous and unfulfilling. I could end up even worse off by forgetting what gives me life and erasing the beauty that lies within the chaos. The gray areas are frightening but have so much potential for a better tomorrow.

By recognizing the possibilities within the unknown, I can accept my existence as a political. I didn't ask for it, but every action justifies this notion. Everyday my voice grows louder, and I will never be silenced. I am proud of my identity and what it represents and so grateful to be alive. I am finally living in full color.

Stubborn

by Charlotte Adams

I am often called stubborn
I will not deny it
My knuckles are too often white from holding onto things so tight
The heels of my shoes are worn out from defiantly digging them into the ground
And my voice is frequently hoarse from arguments gone sour

I am often called stubborn
I get it
It's always something with me
I have been known to stop classes in their tracks
Make dinners uncomfortable
And blow up family parties
It seems that I am incapable of holding my tongue
But in the rare moments that I do
The rest of you suddenly find your voices
You all whisper, you all yell
You ask if I ever stop
If I ever take a break
You tell me I don't have to find it in everything
And the worst of you, those of you who understand the least, tell me to shut up

I am often called stubborn
But did you ever think that maybe I got this way to survive?
That by now I've learned if I let them back in after the first homophobic remark then there's almost a second
And a third
And a fourth
And a fifth

Until I am tired, tired, tired
of trying to teach them to respect me
So I do what's easy
I do what's safe
I cut them out
And if you think I'm being unfair you've probably never had to protect yourself like this
Stubbornness has kept my heart whole for this long
And I don't miss any of the ones I've left behind

I am often called stubborn
But is that supposed to be a bad thing?
Did stubbornness not gain me, a woman, the right to vote?
Did stubbornness not gain me, a queer person, the right to marry?
I'm sorry
But from where I'm standing
Stubbornness doesn't seem all that bad
In fact
It seems like it's given me practically everything that I have

I am often called stubborn
Those close to me know this is to be true
Anyone who has ever been in an argument with me knows that look in my eyes
The look that tells you that this conversation has reached the point of no return
That you will not be rid of me until I have been heard
The look that has made grown men tell me they wouldn't want to get in my way
The look that has made careless family members watch what they say
That look is the quiet before the storm and you know it
Do you know what I'm thinking in that moment?

In that moment I am thinking
What if the activists before me had backed down?
Bit their tongues until they bled?
Allowed themselves to be quietly escorted off the streets?
I act this way because I am constantly reminded of the sacrifices of those before me
That if they can do that then I *have* to do this
I chose the life of an activist
I don't just get to opt out when it gets inconvenient for me
When it gets inconvenient for you
What you so simply call stubbornness I call my duty

I certainly am stubborn
So don't tell me to pick my battles
That is a sure way to guarantee that I will pick one with you
I *do* pick my battles
I just sometimes pick ones you don't want me to
And don't you dare place your finger to my lips and say
"Baby steps, Charlotte"
"Everything has to start somewhere, Charlotte"
That will never calm me down the way you hope it will
It only intensifies everything about me
It only makes me angrier
It only makes me louder
I know everything has to start somewhere
And I'll be damned if it doesn't start with me

So call me stubborn all you want
But don't be surprised if I smile
And say "thank you"

Made in the USA
Middletown, DE
12 June 2021